CROCUS AND COLCHICUM

A HANDBOOK OF
CROCUS AND COLCHICUM
FOR GARDENERS

by

E. A. BOWLES

*with a chapter on changes
of nomenclature by B. L. Burtt*

WATERSTONE · LONDON

First published in 1924.

This edition, with a new preface by Brian Mathew and
colour illustrations, published by Waterstone & Co. Limited in 1985
by kind permission of The Bodley Head Ltd.

The publishers are grateful to the
Harry Smith Horticultural Photographic Collection
for their kind permission to reproduce
the colour photographs in this book.

Cover Design by George Carter.

Printed and bound in Great Britain by
Richard Clay (The Chaucer Press) Ltd,
Bungay, Suffolk

Distributed (except in USA) by
Thames and Hudson Ltd.

ISBN 0 947752 26 9

Contents

Illustrations

ILLUSTRATIONS

Preface

IN AN AGE WHEN books are being published at an astounding rate, on every subject you would care to mention, it is pleasing to see a few 'old friends' which have stood the test of time, and good to see them made available to a new audience by their re-publication.

The Handbook of Crocus and Colchicum is one of these, containing a wealth of practical, botanical and gardening observations which is as valid today as when they were first made by the great man over 60 years ago. Such works can be erudite but stuffy accounts, destined for the dusty monograph sections of botanical libraries; but not so the *Handbook*: Although it is packed with information it is written in a lively style with a delightful turn of phrase, the use of English enjoyable and the descriptions often worth much more to the reader than their strict botanical counterparts. As a botanist I cannot describe, in the terms available to me, the subtle difference in bud shape between *C. tomasinianus* and *C. vernus*, but Bowles could! To quote, '*C. tomasinianus* has a slender flower bud due to the close wrapping of the segments, reminding one of a smart new umbrella compared with the thicker clumsier buds of *C. vernus* which are more of the 'gamp' style'. His analogies are still quoted today, for they have not been bettered, for example the distinctive black specks in the flowers of *C. Pestalozzae* looking like 'tiny pellets of soil fallen into the throat', and the best way to pronounce *C. cvijicii* being to 'imitate a sneeze'!

The whole book conveys the feeling that here was a true naturalist who knew not only his plants but a great deal more about natural history. How many people would notice that the nasty smell of *C. graveolens* contained 'an added whiff of black beetles' or that after years of being dried the flowers were still smelling 'in much the same way as Petrel eggs scent the drawer in which they are kept'.

In the case of *Colchicum* there is still no replacement volume and the *Handbook* remains the standard work. My own studies in Crocus may have added new species and reclassified the genus, but I find that the revered 'Bowles' has a very prominent place on my bookshelf and is frequently thumbed for information, and wistfully admired for the literary excellence contained therein.   BRIAN MATHEW

I

The Crocus in the Garden

THE GENUS CROCUS deserves more attention than it has hitherto received in British gardens.

Three only of its spring-flowering species have become general favourites, and there are still many good gardens in which autumnal and winter-flowering species have never been planted. Yet no other genus of hardy plants contains so many species and varieties that will flower in the open ground during the dullest months of the year.

By planting those now offered by nurserymen an unbroken succession of flowers may be obtained from mid-September until April showers bring such a wealth of other blossom that the gardener no longer needs the lowly Crocus. More peaceful conditions and security for travel in southern Russia and Asia Minor might assist in the reintroduction of several beautiful species, which the greater skill of the modern gardener, with his scree beds, properly drained rock gardens and the alpine house, should add to the number of early autumnal treasures.

The beautiful orange-yellow *C. Scharojanii* and the creamy-white *C. vallicola* from the Caucasus, and some of the Eastern forms of the variable *C. cancellatus*, if successfully established in our gardens, would lengthen the Crocus season by their regular appearance early in August.

The first rains of September ought to bring up sheets of the almost blue flowers of *C. speciosus* in borders and shrubberies, as surely and as suddenly as they do the mushrooms. Any November or December morning on which the sun shines and the ground is free from snow should provide clumps of the lilac or white blossoms of *C. laevigatus* in every British garden that contains a wall, shrub or stone that can cut off the north or east wind from this fragrant species. New Year's Day will generally invite the making of a list of plants in flower if the *CC. chrysanthus, Sieberi, Imperati* and *Korolkowii* have been planted.

It is then a pity that in so many gardens the Crocus season only begins in the latter weeks of February with the Dutch Yellow, and ends a fortnight or so later with the garden-raised forms of *C. vernus*.

A large majority of species are hardy enough to thrive in the open, and are quite as easy to grow well as most flowers that are worth having. Any ground sufficiently well tilled to grow a decent lettuce or onion should grow Crocuses to perfection. The best possible corner of a garden for growing a collection of Crocuses would be, to my mind, a portion of an old kitchen garden open to the south and with a wall or buildings on the north side.

Some, as for instance *CC. speciosus, pulchellus* and *nudiflorus* in autumn, and *Tomasinianus, aureus, vernus* and others flowering in spring, can hold their own in mixed borders or shrubberies, but where choice and rare kinds are to be grown it is safest to give up a long, narrow bed to their use. There the leaves can mature naturally, instead of being overshadowed and choked by the growth of other plants. This too frequently happens where they are planted in rock gardens or herbaceous borders, and their owner ungratefully forgets the pleasure they gave earlier in the year when enjoying the luxurious way herbaceous plants spread over the bare spaces in late April and May. I need hardly warn the Crocus grower against plaiting the green leaves just at the time they are most active in building up the reserve of nutriment in the young corm, when the last thing one should wish is to hasten their decay and so shorten their period of usefulness.

The ideal soil would be one deeply tilled and rich in humus. It would not matter if it were somewhat heavy so long as it was well drained, for most Crocuses like to send their roots down into rich, strong soil, if the corms are lying in a light and warm one. This means that the upper eight or more inches should have coarse sand or sharp river grit mixed with it, and I have found it beneficial to both the plants and the grower if the corms are laid on an inch of sharp sand at planting time, and covered over with another inch-deep layer before the surface soil is replaced. It is a wonderful help at lifting time to find this well-marked stratum of sand with the corms lying in it.

Something between four and six inches seems to be the best depth for planting, but many species, especially *C. aureus* and *C. speciosus*, do not object to being much deeper.

However, as with deeply planted Tulips and Daffodils, though the plant remains vigorous very little if any increase is made. In collecting wild Crocuses I have invariably found them unpleasantly deep, and by the number of their old tunics it was clear that they had been at that depth for some twelve or more seasons, and had never formed more than the one corm each year. These, when grown in garden ground, multiplied rapidly by corm increase, so we may conclude that when it is desired to work up a stock of any variety it is best not to plant very deeply, and to lift the corms annually, cleaning away the old tunics and the withered portion of last year's corm from the base, if it will come away easily and without the use of force.

When a rich display of bloom is desired the replanting can be put off till the third or even fourth year; but if it is noticed that the increase has been great enough to form congested tufts of leaves and the flowers are not as large as they should be, replanting should not be deferred beyond the following August. If planted in straight lines and liberally treated as to sand, it is an easy job to lift the dormant corms during a dry spell in the end of July or early in August, and a very pleasant one if the increase has been plentiful and the size of the new corms is satisfactory.

The autumn-flowering species should be replanted as soon as possible, as some—especially *C. byzantinus*, which prefers moist ground—begin rooting in mid-July. Spring-flowering kinds can be stored safely in a dry, cool place until October if necessary, but are safer and sounder if planted in August.

If it is necessary to plant different kinds close to one another, as in the case of new seedlings of which there are but two or three corms, it is a good plan to alternate those with well-marked differences of corm tunic, for instance, a coriaceous, or annulate form, next to one with a netted or parallel-fibred tunic. I have found this plan of great help in preventing their getting mixed at the next lifting. Slates may be buried between the plantings if it is desired to arrange the bed in square clumps instead of lines, but even with this aid to keeping clean stocks it is better that neighbouring forms should be distinct in their tunics, as then a seedling from the next division is easily detected.

A cold frame given over to Crocuses is a very desirable form of luxury, and the winter-flowering and extreme Southern species can be grown thus to greater perfection—*CC. hyemalis, Tournefortii, Cambessedesii* and *cyprius* need protection, and most of those that flower in November, December and January produce more perfect blossoms under cover than in the open during spells of bad weather. An ordinary brick-sided frame, with a slight slope to the south and the surface of the soil not more than a foot above the natural level, is a delightful adjunct to the Crocus bed. The lights should be opened on all fine days, but closed at night and during very wet or cold weather from October to April. As soon as the leaves have turned yellow towards the end of May the lights should be placed on the frame and raised slightly at the back for ventilation, until the seeds have been collected and the time has come for lifting the roots, which in a frame should be done annually.

The soil in a frame needs an occasional dressing with some fertiliser. I find bone meal is the easiest and safest, as it can be mixed with the soil when it is dug over for replanting, or sprinkled on the surface and watered in at any time, but is most effective while the roots are active. It acts quickly and will help to strengthen the leaves if applied early in autumn, and another but lighter dose in March at the close of the flowering season helps to feed the new corms.

Mr. John Hoog, of Haarlem, tells me that he has found that 'the species of Crocus abhor any nitrogenous manure; basic slag and potash are what they want.'

As the former acts slowly it should be applied to beds or frames with an eye to future benefit and before growth commences.

For herbaceous beds and shrubberies the stronger-growing kinds can be planted in large clumps and drifts. Soil should be removed to the depth of six inches and the corms laid on the bottom of the hole at the space of an inch from each other. It is customary to plant Crocuses as edgings to borders in rather formal lines or circles, but a charming effect is produced by planting some hundreds of one kind under deciduous shrubs, or at the back of borders between clumps of strong-growing herbaceous plants that do not cover the ground with their leaves earlier than the middle of May, and thus allowing time for the Crocus leaves to mature in an open space.

The Dutch Yellow, in my opinion, never looks better than when planted in a generously planned drift, towards the back of a large border, or round the stem of a leafless *Azalea mollis,** Deutzia, etc. All the florists' forms of *C. vernus* are suitable for this work, and *C. Tomasinianus* once planted should be allowed to spread naturally by seed as far as it will under groups of roses or other summer-leafing shrubs. *C. speciosus* is the best of all the autumn-flowering Crocuses for wide plantings, and does not object to an occasional digging over of the bed and the consequent deep burial of the corms. Only the stronger growers should be tried in grass and none succeeds better than forms of *C. vernus* and the Dutch Yellow. I have always advised that they should be kept separate, or at any rate the yellow planted only among white varieties; but a charming planting of irregular colonies, each of one kind, under some trees in a friend's garden taught me that if the yellow are planted in separate groups, instead of being scattered among the purples, they can be very effective.

The quality of grass differs so greatly that my rather poor success with the many species I have tried in a rough meadow need not discourage others with a finer brand of turf. I used to give bundles of rogues and mixed seedlings to Mr. Wilks to plant in his wild garden at Shirley, and in his grass they flourished and spread most delightfully. The soil there is a fine sand, and he used to say of it that it was so light that if he threw it up in the air it would never come down again, and naturally the grass on it is scanty and fine.

Where the turf is not coarse, and the ground well drained and open to sunshine, I advise planting *CC. Tomasinianus, aureus, chrysanthus, Sieberi* and *versicolor* as well as *C. vernus* for spring, and *CC. Kotschyanus, speciosus, nudiflorus* and *longiflorus* for autumn.

The chief enemies of Crocuses are mice, and it is necessary to be ever on the watch where large stocks are grown. A rabbit

* Now called *Rhododendron molle.*

can do much mischief in a night or two in early spring, and pheasants, if once they discover the delight of eating Crocus corms, will scratch up and devour great numbers. Small birds occasionally learn that after frosty weather the upper soil is loosened, and a pull at the young leaves will bring up a seedling of one or two years of age, and the owner finds the leaves, but not the tender, young corm. Sparrows for certain, and chaffinches I suspect, are the chief offenders. Black cotton stretched across the beds is the next best preventive to killing the birds.

In dry, frosty weather birds pull the blossoms to pieces for the sake of the drop of honey in the throat of the flower. Pans of water set about are good for both birds and flowers, but even with this attention black cotton may also be necessary.

Mice need fighting in all months and by any means. Break-back traps baited with Brazil nut are very useful weapons. Nor should one neglect the aid of cats, poison, virus, sunken jars or any other method of destroying the Field Vole, which nibbles off leaves and buds, and the Long-Tailed Wood Mouse, which digs up and devours the corms.

In frames the larvæ of the Turnip Moth, *Agrotis segetum*, is in some seasons a great trouble as it bores into the newly formed corms during June and July, and one does not think of its evil ways until lifting time, when much mischief has been done. The Yellow Underwing, *Triphaena pronuba*, and Angle-shade Moth, *Phlogophora meticulosa*, often lay eggs in the frames and the larvæ attack the leaves and buds in autumn and early spring. They hide below ground in the daytime, so the best way of catching them is to visit the frame after dark with a good electric lamp, or if that is too strenuous a job the evil things may be trapped by making a round hole with one's finger in the soil, close by the evidences of damage, and plugging the top of it with a lettuce leaf or juicy little brussels sprout. It is never long before the caterpillar finds the bait and avails itself of the provided bedchamber below it, and the inquiring finger detects a plump body at the bottom of the hole.

The most exciting part of growing Crocuses is the raising of seedlings, although it needs patience and a preliminary wait of three years before the first flowers are produced.

If you wish to cross varieties or species you should grow some in pots sunk in the ground that they may be brought into a house at flowering time; but if you are not too proud or stiff to kneel down on the ground, much can be done in the open-air bed or frame. It is necessary to open a bud and to remove the anthers before they have dehisced or shed their pollen. The segments can be turned outwards for this purpose by finger and thumb, finger outwards and pressing the convex surface of the outside of a segment till it becomes concave. The anthers having been removed with a pair of forceps, pollen from another flower may be rubbed on the stigma, and the segments turned back again to their normal condition. If brought into the house flowers will open quickly near a lamp or fire. A neighbour made some successful crossings in the open on dull days, and in the evening after his return from London, by placing a bell glass over a lamp till the air inside was heated and then placing it over the Crocus, which opened quickly.

Of course these purposely planned crossings must be protected afterwards from the visits of bees by muslin covers. Of late years I have left it to the bees to arrange the eugenics of many Crocuses and they have done it so well that plentiful variation has resulted.

The seed capsules are below ground until just before ripening. From early in May onward to July a watch should be kept for their appearance above ground. Those species that flower in early autumn, such as *C. Kotschyanus* and *C. speciosus*, ripen their seeds first. It is best to gather them before the capsule splits, as the seeds scatter soon after. They can be easily dried in old envelopes or small boxes. *C. caspius* and *C. Korolkowii* do not push their capsules above the soil, so they should be looked for when lifting the corms.

Seeds are best sown no later than the first week in September. We find it convenient to sow in small pots which are afterwards sunk in the soil and left undisturbed for two years.

Then they should be turned out, and, if all is well, a good crop of cormlets about the size of a small pea will be found at the bottom of each pot. These can be planted in rows in the open ground as one would treat adult corms, and left till they flower, which a few may do in the following season, but most of them

B

in the fourth year from sowing. The first three barren years soon pass away, and then it is good to stand before the seed bed on a sunny morning and see the rows of open blossoms with here and there one that is unlike its brethren and perhaps anything else we have seen before. A pure white seedling of *C. Sieberi* rewarded me for thirty years of patience, and I still hope for further pleasant surprises.

II

Botanical Characters

ANYONE who would spend half an hour in a careful examination and dissection of a living Crocus plant at flowering time, or just after, would be amply repaid for his trouble. It would be best to select three of the larger species, say a garden form of *C. vernus*; the Dutch Yellow, a form of *C. aureus*; and the Scotch Crocus, *C. biflorus*.

The Tunic. First notice the tunic or wrappings of the so-called 'bulb,' which is really a corm. A pocket lens will show that the tow-like strands enclosing the *C. vernus* are netted, that is the fibres branch and are joined together again. Most likely one or more of the upper and outermost wrappings will be completely skeletonised with clear spaces between the meshes of the fibre. The lower ones should show a membranous ground-work in which the fibres are embedded, and that, at about two-thirds of the depth of the corm, the fibres become free, straight and parallel, curving inwards towards the base and allowing a clear passage between their strands for the roots. A dry specimen in autumn should show what is called the basal tunic, which in *C. vernus* is star shaped, composed of unbranched stiff fibres radiating from a circular, central plate. Its fibres enter among those of the main tunic forming a complete wrapping and yet allowing the roots, which spring from a definite zone at the base, to escape between the strands.

In the Dutch Yellow the tunic is of a redder brown and its membrane is stouter and more persistent, so that unless a portion of a two years old tunic is still undecayed there will be no free fibres showing in the upper portion. It will be noticed that the tunic is prolonged upwards into withered, brown points, called the cap, a characteristic feature in some species, and wanting in others. This cap helps us to trace the origin of the corm tunics, for it closely resembles the already browning tips of the scale leaves that encircle the main shoot of leaves and flowers. By slitting this tube of scale leaves longitudinally and peeling the scales downwards it will be seen that they become thick, juicy skins which cover the young corm, and finally dry and form the tunic. When all four, or more, sheathed scales have been peeled down it will be seen that the leaves are the next organs revealed, and that their white lower portions widen out and are fleshy like the bases of the sheathing scales, but that they only enclose a small section of the young corm, and are joined to it by their bases at about one-third of its depth. The tunic then is formed of the bases of sheathing scales and leaves, its fibres representing a continuation of those of the leafy bodies. Tunics vary so greatly in their fibrous skeleton and membranous base that they form a valuable aid for the recognition of species.

The tunic of *C. vernus* is termed a finely reticulated tunic, while in those of *C. Sieberi* and *C. susianus* the fibres are coarser and the interstices larger, providing examples of coarse reticulation. In *C. Fleischeri* the fibres are silky and interwoven in a manner reminiscent of the tunic of *Iris reticulata* or *Iris Sisyrinchium*. In *C. aureus* and many others the fibres are parallel throughout their length, but in many species slightly reticulated fibres occur in the upper third of the tunic and parallel fibres below.

Membranous tunics without fibres are found in *CC. hyemalis*, *caspius*, *Boryi* and others, but towards the base they split into strap-like divisions which when partially decayed closely resemble fibres.

Hard leathery tunics are found in *C. lævigatus* and some of the species related to the Scotch Crocus. Examination of the latter will show that the lower portion of the corm is enclosed by concentric rings of tunic, hard and horny like the main tunic, and armed on their upper edges with short teeth that assist them in clinging to each other and clothing the corm.

The Corm. Having removed the tunics we find two rounded, solid bodies, one on the top of the other. The lower will be rather wrinkled, brownish, and flattened at its poles; the upper pearly-white, smaller, somewhat conical and attached at its base to the lower. The upper corm divided vertically and transversely will be found to be solid, and composed of cellular tissue and starch, somewhat similar to the kernel of a nut, and represents the stored material for the growing plant. It will enlarge at the expense of the older and lower corm, which is already becoming flabby and wrinkled. In some species several new corms may be formed at the apex of the old, and in others from various points of its circumference. The corm represents a compressed, underground stem, an extreme modification of the stem-tuber, the new corms being branches formed annually on the old. It differs from a bulb in being a solid body instead of one formed of scales.

The stem is generally represented by no more than a flat, basal plate in a bulb, but forms the main portion of a corm. The investing scales of both represent leaves or leaf bases. In a bulb they are fleshy, being stored with nutriment, while in a Crocus corm they are but dry skins forming the tunic. Thus the difference between a bulb and a corm is really only one of degree and gradations occur between the two.

Scale Leaves. Next in order come the scale leaves, or sheathing leaves of some writers. These, we have seen, envelop the young corm with their bases, but as they rise above it assume the form of a tube. They are three to five in number and the innermost is invariably the longest. For the most part they are composed of a stout colourless membrane, but the longest is in some species green at its tip; in others the tips widen out into papery blades.

These sheathing leaves serve both to protect and to strengthen the young shoot and assist it to pierce through the hardest soil in a quite wonderful way.

The Leaves. When this tube is slit down by the knife, the leaves, from one to a dozen or more according to the species, are the next organs within. Colourless and strap shaped in their lowest portion they become wider, with both edges rolled back. Mature leaves vary much in different species, but most of them have a well-defined, raised central rib, or keel, on the back, corresponding with a white-surfaced groove on the upper side. The blades on either side, rolled at first, generally open out till they become almost flat at maturity. In some species there is a fringe of fine hairs on the edges of both keel and blades when the leaves are said to be ciliated; leaves without hairs are described as glabrous.

Those of *C. aureus* are ciliated, while in *C. vernus* they are glabrous. Two species, *C. carpetanus* and *C. nevadensis*, have peculiar leaves in which the blades are no more than slightly prominent ridges on the edges of the semicylindrical keel, while in *CC. Scharojanii, vallicola* and *Kotschyanus* the keel is as wide as the blade and a transverse section presents a somewhat cruciform appearance. In many autumn-flowering species the leaves do not appear above ground until spring or shortly after the flowers, but this is only the case so far as I know with one spring-flowering species—*C. gargaricus*.

Basal Spathe. Springing from the centre of the young corm we find the flower scape and notice a marked difference between that of *C. vernus* and *C. aureus*, for in the former a transparent, membranous spathe grows between the scape and the leaves, wrapping its lower two-thirds in a protecting tube. This is the basal spathe and is present in some species but is absent in others, as in the case of the Dutch Yellow. Those species possessing the basal spathe form Herbert's Division I *Involucrati*, those without it his Division III *Nudiflori*. He was doubtful about its presence in two species, *C. Heuffelianus* (*C. banaticus*) and *C. Tomasinianus*, and placed them in a Division II *Subnudi*. The basal spathe, however, is generally present in both these species, and the nearly allied one, described on page 77 under 'C. Heuffelianus,' is the only one in which I have found some specimens lacking a basal spathe, while the greater number have it.

Proper Spathe. At flowering time the scape, or flower stalk, is very short and in some species almost suppressed, but lengthens as the seeds ripen, so as to bear the capsule up above ground. The ovary is marked with purple at its top in many species, and growing out of its base will be found either one or two spathes of thin transparent membrane, which wrap the young bud until it emerges to open. The outer of these is tubular, and the inner, when present, is generally strap shaped or ligulate. They are called the proper spathes and the presence or absence of the inner one affords good specific characters in most cases, but *CC. Salzmannii, serotinus, Imperati, Biliottii* and some varieties of *C. aureus* vary in this respect.

The presence of an inner proper spathe is described as *diphyllous*, its absence as *monophyllous*, and these two characters are correlated very markedly with the presence or absence of the basal spathe. All the known species of the *Nudiflori* have diphyllous proper spathes except *C. gargaricus* and *C. cyprius*, but six of the *Involucrati* are always diphyllous besides a few that are so occasionally.

Perianth Tube. The most remarkable features of a Crocus flower are the enormous length of the style and also of the tube that carries the flower above ground at flowering time. The latter is called the perianth tube and serves instead of a stalk.

They may be compared with the similar structures in a Colchicum and *Iris unguicularis*. The top of the perianth tube is called the throat and swells outwards from the point where the stamens are inserted on the three outer segments. The inner surface of the throat is either furnished with tufts of fine hairs, when it is called bearded, or is entirely glabrous, affording yet another very useful pair of specific characters, that only fail to be invariable in *C. vernus* and occasionally in some other species of that group.

The Perianth. The perianth is a botanical term for the sepals and petals of a flower taken together and regarded as surrounding the essential organs of reproduction. It is more especially used for those flowers in which the outer whorl of floral leaves, the sepals, are much like the inner whorl, the petals, and has been generally used for the Crocus, the three larger and outer floral leaves, considered to represent sepals, being called the outer segments. These may be compared with the falls of an Iris, while the inner segments of the perianth, representing petals, correspond with the standards in the Iris. As a rule the outer segments of a Crocus are longer and more pointed than the inner, and in one, *C. byzantinus*, they are so much longer and wider that the flower looks somewhat like an Iris.

In the greater number of species the outer surfaces of the three outer segments are either of duller colouring than their inner surfaces and also than both sides of the inner segments; or they may be striped; marked with featherings, that is striped with short lines branching from the main line; or again freckled, or suffused, with darker markings. In the case of white or lilac forms these markings are purple, but in the yellow species they are mostly brown.

In all cases the duller or darker external coloration renders
the unopened bud less conspicuous. The grey outer surface of
C. Tomasinianus may be compared with that of *Iris unguicularis*,
for in both plants the closed buds are not easily detected on
a dull day, but become very conspicuous the moment they
respond to warmth or sunlight and display their inner surfaces.

The same sudden transformation occurs with *C. Imperati*
and its relations; the buff ground and dark purple featherings
of their outer surface hide them until contrasted with the
brilliant mauve of their interior.

This dull coloration when closed would afford protection
from hungry predatory animals on their native slopes, but the
same sunshine that would open them and render them conspicuous from afar would entice the chilled insects out of their
hiding places in search of pollen or honey. So the open and
gleaming Crocus of a sunny hour attracts insects to assist in its
cross fertilisation, and with the return of chilly or dark hours,
which drive the insects back to shelter, the Crocus shuts itself
up into its former obscurity.

In some species, such as *C. susianus* and *C. Balansae*, with much
dark colour on the exterior, this change from conspicuous
flashing colour to a cryptic blending with the surroundings is as
complete as in the case of the Red Underwing Moth (*Catocala
nupta*). On the wing the scarlet underwings render it attractive
to birds, and I have seen the moth pursued by sparrows when
I have disturbed it, but so soon as it settles on a willow tree, and
the grey, upper wings are folded over the scarlet underwings,
it is so nearly indistinguishable from the bark of the tree that
the bird flies on looking for a scarlet moth.

The effect of external stripes or featherings may be compared
with the markings of tigers, and just as the animal is protected
by its similarity to light and shade in jungles of tall grass, so
the flower resembles bare ground crossed by its own leaves or
those of grasses as well as by their shadows.

The Stamens. The stamens are only three in number and are
set upon the outer segments. They vary very much among the
species. The anthers are as a rule about twice the length of
their filaments, and with the exception of *C. byzantinus*, in which
they open *introrsely*, all the known species have anthers which

open extrorsely, that is to say on the outward side. When the throat is yellow so is the filament, except in *C. cyprius* and *C. Hartmannianus*, in which it is scarlet. When yellow is absent from the throat the filaments are white, or slightly tinted with cream colour or lilac. In most species they are more or less papillose and in a few, such as *C. Tournefortii* and *C. pulchellus*, are covered with glandular hairs.

The anthers are mostly yellow or orange. In *CC. Boryi, Tournefortii, pulchellus, ochroleucus, Kotschyanus, vallicola, laevigatus, Veneris* and a hitherto undescribed species from Palestine, they are white. In *C. chrysanthus* they frequently, but not invariably, show conspicuous black tips to the pointed barbs at the base, and in some forms of that species and a few others they may be variably stained with brown or grey.

In the variety *Foxii* of *C. hyemalis*, var. *micranthus* of *C. reticulatus*, in *C. Crewei* and a few others, they are quite black before dehiscence; but after the opening of the valves, and the liberation of the yellow pollen, the black is not so conspicuous. *C. aureus* has the largest anthers compared with its size and *C. Cambessedesii* possibly the shortest.

The Pistil. Owing to the length of the perianth tube the style is necessarily disproportionately long for the size of the flower, and may be compared with that of *Iris unguicularis*. In most species the style divides more or less at the level of the bases or summits of the anthers into three stigmatic branches, which show such distinct variations of form and colour that their different types have been made much use of as specific characters.

On the strength of these variations Baker divided the Crocuses into three sections:

1. Holostigma, with entire stigmata.
2. Odontostigma, with stigmata toothed or slightly divided.
3. Schizostigma, with stigmata deeply divided and branching.

Unfortunately this simple arrangement does not always group the closely allied species together, and in some, as in *C. longiflorus*, there is much variation in the amount of division of the stigmata.

The extreme case of undivided stigmata is seen in the

cultivated form of *C. sativus*, from which the long, red, club-shaped stigmatic branches are collected and dried to become the drug Saffron.

In *C. medius* the divisions are as fine as hairs and very numerous. *C. aureus* and *C. chrysanthus* exhibit good examples of toothed stigmata. Their stigmatic branches are more or less flattened or funnel shaped with short stigmatic bodies forming a fringe along the edge. Various shades of yellow, from cream colour to scarlet, occur in the stigmata and in some species, especially in *C. aureus* and *C. chrysanthus*, individuals vary greatly in the range of colouring. The variety *leucostigma* of *C. vernus*, though otherwise richly coloured, shows a kind of albinism in its white stigma.

Crocus nevadensis regularly has a colourless stigma. In *C. carpetanus* it is tinted with lilac, while in *C. byzantinus* the finely divided branches are normally purple, but become straw colour in the white form.

In most cases the stigmatic branches overtop or spread beyond the anthers, are receptive for pollen at the first opening of the flower, and sometimes even before the dehiscence of the anthers they protrude from an unopened bud. Thus the Crocus is mostly protogynous, but the stigmata of unfertilised blossoms remain sound and receptive for some days after the pollen has been shed or the segments have faded. In gardens Hive Bees visit Crocuses to collect either pollen or honey. The honey rises as high as the throat in the tube, and therefore much of it is available for an insect with a short proboscis. Autumnal species are much visited by the Silver Y Moth, *Plusia gamma*. Hive Bees in search of honey generally alight on the showy and prominent stigmata, thus frequently dusting them with pollen adhering to their under surface and procured from another flower, and so effecting cross-pollination.

I have watched the flowers of *C. speciosus* in late September and have frequently observed bees alight on the outspread segments and proceed to the anthers to strip them of their pollen, which they do without coming in contact with the stigma. However, this may not be the case with the bees of the native countries of this Crocus. Bumble-bees generally grasp the stigmata upon arrival at the flowers.

The ovary is buried safely away below ground at the time of flowering but shortly after fertilisation is carried upward by the growth of its supporting scape or flower stalk, until it lies in the hollow of the surrounding leaves, just above the level of the soil where it is reached by light and warmth. Except in *C. caspius* and *C. Korolkowii*, in which the capsules remain below ground even after the seed is ripe, the scape elongates rapidly in May or June and raises the capsule above the leaves, where, being dried by the sunshine, it splits into three valves and the seeds are scattered around the parent plant. The seeds vary in colour in the different species, those of *C. sativus* being deep crimson-purple. In *C. chrysanthus* they are red, in *C. biflorus* buff, and brown in *C. Korolkowii*.

Most of them have a fleshy caruncle, and judging by the distance from the parent at which seedlings frequently appear, I think they are carried off by ants, and perhaps worms, which eat this fleshy protuberance and assist in spreading the plants.

The result of our examination should teach us that the Crocus is an Irid, as proclaimed at a glance, by its having no more than three stamens, and confirmed on further observation by the position of the ovary below and outside the perianth tube; and by the division of the pistil into three branches.

It is useful to compare the flower with that of a Colchicum, a member of the Lily family, in which there are six stamens, the ovary is enclosed in the base of the perianth tube and the three pistils, though occasionally adhering for a short space of their length, are separate at their base and unbranched at their tips.

In the Crocus the most outstanding features are : the extreme reduction of stem and flower stalk and the consequent development of a long perianth tube; the keeled leaves with rolled blades ! and the protection of the ovary by its underground position. The reason for these modifications seems to me best understood if regarded as fitting the plant for a short period of active growth, in which it becomes fully prepared to do its work rapidly when the right time arrives after a long period of rest, and to make the most of short spells of fine weather in autumn, winter or spring. Thus the floral and foliar organs are completely formed before the drought of summer arrests activity and are ready to respond immediately to the combined invitations of warmth and moisture. In the case of autumnal species, chiefly found at lower levels or in southern climates, this would be the coming of the autumn rains, and for alpine species the melting of the snow in spring.

It is worth noting that although the flowers and leaves of such species as *CC. chrysanthus, vernus, aureus* and other spring-flowering species are as fully formed by August as those of *CC. speciosus, nudiflorus, cancellatus* and other autumnal species, no amount of forcing will induce the former to flower before the New Year, and the latter will start to throw out their flowers at their accustomed seasons, even if kept unplanted in a dry atmosphere.

This may point to a southern, and possibly North African, origin of the genus, where the dominating condition was the early prevailing drought, before which growth must be completed, and suggests that the wanderings of modified derivatives to high altitudes have been accompanied by their acquiring a fixed habit of remaining dormant until the melting of the snow.

The ancestor of the genus then might have been some Romulea or an intermediate form that could be the common ancestor of both. Romulea differs from Crocus mostly in the possession of a well-defined flower stalk that raises the ovary above ground at flowering time, and also in the absence of a keel and rolled blades in the leaf. *C. carpetanus* in Spain, and *C. nevadensis*—common to Spain and North Africa—approach Romulea fairly closely as to the leaf structure, and in the latter the shape and shyness of opening of the flowers greatly resemble certain species of Romulea.

I should like to think that the Crocus as now known was derived from a Romulea-like ancestor, leaving links of its descent in *CC. nevadensis, Cambessedesii,* and through *C. minimus* and its allied species on the one hand developed to *CC. Imperati* and *etruscus,* and so onward to the reticulate section and such as *C. Sieberi.* While on the other hand through *C. versicolor* it would arrive at *C. vernus* and its closely related species.

C. carpetanus seems to lead nowhere, but again from *C. nevadensis* we can trace a resemblance in *C. Salzmannii* also common to Spain and Africa, and from it a chain through

C. Clusii of Portugal to *CC. asturicus* and *nudiflorus*, autumnal forms found in Western Europe.

In the curiously Iris-like *C. byzantinus* we may see traces of a line of development which through *Iris (Gynandriris) Sisyrinchium* led on to the Bearded Irises, in which the beard may be analogous to the tufts of hairs found in the throats of many Crocuses.

III

The Spanish Group

A DISTINCT group of five closely allied autumn-flowering species is distributed over south-western France to the coasts of Spain and Portugal, with two, *C. Salzmannii* and *C. Clusii*, occurring both in Spain and Morocco.

These five species have so many similar characters that they have been much confused by authors. They all belong to Dean Herbert's 'Division I' *Involucrati*, as they have a basal spathe; *Salzmannii* and *serotinus* sometimes have a second and inner proper spathe, otherwise all are monophyllous; and normally their flowers are lilac with yellow anthers and orange stigmata, they can be distinguished thus:

1. { Leafless at flowering time.   *C. nudiflorus.*
   { Leaves developed at flowering time.   2.

2. { Leaves just appearing with flowers.   *C. asturicus.*
   { Leaves well developed before flowers.   3.

3. { Tunic finely reticulated.   *C. Clusii.*
   { Tunic membranous with parallel fibres.   4.

4. { Flowers plain lilac.   *C. Salzmannii.*
   { Flowers striped.   *C. serotinus.*

Although this key should serve for distinguishing typical specimens it may fail in the case of some mysterious intermediate forms recently introduced, the native localities of which are not recorded. There still remains much to be learnt about the autumnal Crocuses of Central Spain and the Middle Atlas.

So eminent a botanist as Sir Joseph Hooker, when dealing with *C. Salzmannii* (t. 6000 of the *Botanical Magazine*), wrote:
> 'belonging to the same section of the Genus as the Portuguese *C. serotinus* and so near to it specifically that I doubt its proving more than a variety of the plant. . . . *C. Clusii* is another form of *C. serotinus*.'

Maw in *The Genus Crocus*, p. 100, wrote that: 'Looking at

the confusion that exists in herbaria and in the published descriptions of the Spanish autumnal Croci it is impossible to rely on any record of *serotinus*.'

Among these puzzling forms are those distributed by Dammann of Naples as *C. graecus* and the very similar *C. Salzmannii* var. *erectophyllus*. They vary, perhaps seasonally, in the degree of development of leaves before flowers and in colour. In the smaller size of corm and the finer fibres of the tunic they are more like *C. Clusii* than *C. Salzmannii*—the name *graecus* is a synonym of the var. *Cartwrightianus* of *C. sativus*, which is plentiful in Greece. I have failed to trace this false *graecus* to a wild source, but feel certain it has a western, not an oriental, area.

Some large corms were sent to me from Granada and I hoped they might prove to be the *C. granatensis* of Boissier, described but not figured in Maw's monograph, which like *C. nudiflorus* should be leafless when in flower. These had well-developed leaves reaching almost to the throat of the handsome lilac flowers, which were much like those of *C. Salzmannii*, but the coarse parallel fibres of their corm tunic and the stiff, erect leaves suggested an extra robust form of the mysterious *erectophyllus*. Unfortunately they were less hardy and I have lost them.

An autumnal exploration of the Sierra Nevada and mountains of Central Spain might well repay a collector and produce some valuable additions to gardens and the knowledge of this puzzling group of Crocuses.

C. nudiflorus was first validly published by Sir James Smith in the first edition of the work generally known as Sowerby's *English Botany*, Sowerby having drawn the plates. It is widely distributed in the Pyrenees and is the plant described as *Crocus pyrenaeus purpureus* in Parkinson's *Paradisus* (1629). Dean Herbert preferred the name *pyrenaeus* on account of its belonging to his 'Division I *Involucrati*, species with a basal involucre or spathe'—while he designated those without the basal spathe as *Nudiflori*. The name, however, refers to the absence of leaves at flowering time, and this is a well-marked feature of *C. nudiflorus*.

Occurring on both sides of the Pyrenees it is very plentiful

in south-western France near Bayonne, Biarritz, St. Jean de
Luz, the Landes and Pau. In Spain it occurs in the Asturias,
near Gijon and Santander.

I found it so plentiful near Bayonne and Luchon that it was
scarcely possible to dig up any plant without finding small
corms of the Crocus in the soil. It is a very handsome and hardy
plant but not often seen in gardens and seldom offered by
nurserymen. This may be due to its curious method of increase
by underground stolons, which hitherto has only been noticed
in two other species, *C. lazicus* and *C. gargaricus*, the former of
which has never been introduced to cultivation. *C. gargaricus*
forms recognisable and well-shaped though very small corms
at the end of slender white stolons; *C. nudiflorus*, however,
bears such curiously shaped stolons that anyone seeing them
for the first time might be pardoned for mistaking them
for some evil form of stoloniferous grass, or even for the pupa
of an insect.

They vary a great deal in size and shape, but in their first
season are more or less vermiform, with bands and rings of
darker skin of the nature of the tunic of a mature corm. They
vary from half an inch to two or more inches in length, and in
gardens seem to take two or three seasons to form flowering
corms. For this reason a newly planted group may not flower
in the second year, nor for a season or two afterwards, and then
may appear at some distance from the original site.

Thus it is best planted in borders or in turf, where it need not
be disturbed and can be allowed to wander and colonise as
it pleases.

The large, rich purple flowers of the Pyrenean form appear in
September, but those from Asturias come late in October and
continue throughout November in some seasons. They are
larger than their nearest relative, *C. asturicus*, and may be
distinguished by their brighter orange and more finely divided
stigmata, glabrous throat, and also by the absence of leaves,
which though occasionally not very evident at first in
C. asturicus may generally be detected just within the sheathing
scales. Beautiful white forms are occasionally found, either
without any tinge of colour or with purple markings at the
throat. I have a pale lilac variety which does not appear before

Bonfire Night, and also a seedling so nearly white that it reminds me of the 'lavender kid gloves' of my youth.

The corm is rather small with a tunic of parallel fibre. Like the others of this group the basal spathe is present and the proper spathe monophyllous. The leaves, not produced until spring, are rather long and coarse.

It has become naturalised in several English counties and was at one time very plentiful in meadows near Nottingham. Unfortunately for the Crocus this has now become a built-up area. I have been told that a few flowers of this brave little die-hard push up annually between the paving stones.

It is still happy and plentiful on hillside grassland near Halifax in Yorkshire.

In *The Naturalist*, 1950 (pp. 133-41), there is a very interesting article by W. B. Crump and W. A. Sledge on the history of *C. nudiflorus*, ' The Halifax Autumn Crocus,' in Britain. This gives the conclusions of the late William Bunting Crump (1868-1950) who was a keen Yorkshire naturalist and historian and who interested himself in the matter for over fifty years. Earlier articles by him appeared in the *Halifax Naturalist* of 1889, the *Yorkshire Post* of October 1st, 1904, and the *Yorkshire Observer* of October 18th, 1909. Crump pointed out that all the localities in which this Crocus, *C. nudiflorus*, is naturalised in Britain occur within a circle drawn round Nottingham, Warwick, Shrewsbury, Preston and Halifax. He noticed that in the Halifax area the Crocus is always found in the meadows near the hill farmsteads and that many of these were formerly the property of the Knights of St. John of Jerusalem, and the double cross, the symbol of that Order, is still to be seen on some of the old buildings. His surmise is that the Crocus was distributed by their agents and because these upland farms seldom had gardens it was most likely planted in the pastures close to the house for the sake of the saffron that could be obtained from the stigmata. But it is evident that it is not indigenous in Britain as it occurs nowhere in northern France. If it were more easily procurable it should be planted widely, and especially in grassy slopes and well-drained meadows. There is a fine form, deeply coloured, large and early flowering, well established in the wild garden at Wisley. Pyrenean peasants

C

call it 'le fleur des dettes' as it flowers at the time when they settle their money affairs. *C. nudiflorus* is figured in *Bot. Mag.*, n.s., t. 169 (1951).

C. asturicus was described by Herbert, but his acquaintance with it was imperfect, and he is in error in stating that it produces its offsets on runners. As I know it from mountains near Gijon in Asturias, it flowers before *C. nudiflorus* collected in the same neighbourhood. It is known there as 'Espanta Pastores,' 'The Terror of Shepherds,' as its appearance after the first autumn rains proclaims the coming of winter.

The flowers are smaller and more pointed than those of *C. nudiflorus*, vary in their shades of purple or lilac and are frequently slightly striped at the throat. White forms are very seldom found, but are very beautiful and desirable, especially when marked with purple at the throat.

It forms a round corm nearly an inch in diameter with parallel fibres in its thin tunic, and closely resembles *C. nudiflorus*, but can always be recognised by the tips of the young leaves appearing with, or soon after, the flowers, and by its bearded throat.

It grows well in open, sunny situations, but is much beloved of field mice. It promises to hold its own in meadow grass, but is not so robust a species as *C. nudiflorus*.

C. Salzmannii of J. Gay is a strong-growing, large species, and remarkably hardy considering that it occurs in southern Spain, near Malaga and at Gibraltar, and in northern Africa near Tangier.

It forms the largest corms of any western species of Crocus and they frequently reach a diameter of about two inches. The tunic is very abundant, soft and, for the most part, membranous, rather like soft wood shavings, but contains fine parallel fibres. This soft tunic and the size of the corm unfortunately make it attractive to mice, and they will dig out a clump in late summer and soon leave nothing but the tunic. The leaves are four inches or more in length by the flowering time, which is about the middle of October. The flowers are freely borne, but though large are of rather thin substa .ce and a washy pale lilac in colour.

C. Clusii was so named by the Swiss botanist J. Gay apparently to connect it with the *Crocum Montanum I* of Clusius's *Historia*, p. 208, and a figure on p. 209 which shows two flowering specimens, one with short leaves, while in the other they are only slightly emerging from the sheaths. The tunic is missing from the left-hand figure but clearly shows parallel fibres in the other.

It is plentiful in western Spain and Portugal, and is therefore the most western of all Crocuses.

It grows in woodland, and makes a fine show near Cintra, Lisbon and Oporto. It is not very robust in cultivation and perhaps is more suited for a cold frame than the open ground, as it flowers in October.

The presence of long leaves at flowering time, its rather small, deep purple flowers and a reticulated corm tunic distinguish it from its neighbours. Variations of colour are not common, and a friend who kindly searched for them on my behalf near Cintra found only two with white flowers, and one pale lilac form with fine featherings, among the hundreds then in flower.

C. serotinus was described by Salisbury and figured in t. 30 (1806) of his *Paradisus Londinensis*, and also in t. 1267 (1810) of the *Botanical Magazine*, but in both cases from garden specimens. It is described as representing the *Crocum Montanum* of Clusius from rocky places on the coast of Portugal, but Clusius's figure and description seems to apply more correctly to what we now regard as *C. Clusii*, as figured by Maw. It is a mysterious plant, which was apparently fairly plentiful in gardens a century since, but is now very scarce, if not lost. The last living specimen I saw was in the collection of Crocuses grown in pots at Glasnevin. It is unknown at present from any wild source, and may be no more than a garden form of its nearest relation *C. Salzmannii*, with a late-flowering habit and striped flowers. It should flower in November and December, and, as I grew it in a cold frame twenty years ago, was a very ornamental plant, but difficult to keep in health and vigour. The figures alluded to above are much too blue in colouring; as I knew it, it was a soft lilac with much-branched featherings of a slightly deeper and more rosy hue on the outer segments.

Croci occur in the neighbourhood of Gibraltar and also at

about 6,000 feet on the upper plateau of the Middle Atlas which have been regarded as either *C. Clusii* or *C. serotinus*. Their flowers are normally of a uniform pale shade of lilac, but in both localities specimens have been found in which the outer segments are distinctly marked with purple featherings. Those I have seen closely resembled the figure of *C. serotinus* on Maw's plate VIII, and also the striped form referred to above found among *C. Clusii* near Cintra.

I should like to believe one such striped variety was the origin of the *C. serotinus* of Salisbury, but all of those I have seen had monophyllous proper spathes, while Salisbury stated that his plant could be immediately distinguished by having two bracts under the pericarpium. However, concerning the garden-grown specimens which provided the only living material he recognised as *C. serotinus*, Maw wrote that the proper spathe, though generally monophyllous, was occasionally accompanied by a ligulate bract.

As capsules and seeds were unknown, it may well be that Salisbury's *serotinus* was a clone of a selected feathered form of some self-coloured species.

IV

Eastern Leafless Autumnal Species

IT is convenient to group together certain species whose chief common characters are that their flowers appear in autumn before their leaves, and that all (with the exception of *C. medius* from the Maritime Alps) inhabit eastern Europe, Asia Minor or Palestine.

In other characters they belong to widely different sections, but for recognition in the garden they may be distinguished by this rough key:

1.	Segments approximately of the same size.	2.
	Inner segments much shorter than outer.	*C. byzantinus.*
2.	Flowers white.	3.
	Flowers coloured.	4.
3.	Throat all yellow.	*C. cancellatus.*
	Throat with two orange spots on each segment.	*C. vallicola.*
4.	Flowers yellow.	*C. Scharojanii.*
	Flowers lilac.	5.
5.	Tunic annulate.	6.
	Tunic not annulate.	7.
6.	Anthers yellow.	*C. speciosus.*
	Anthers white.	*C. pulchellus.*
7.	Tunic reticulated.	8.
	Tunic membranous.	9.
8.	Proper spathe monophyllous.	*C. medius.*
	Proper spathe diphyllous.	*C. cancellatus.* var. *cilicicus.*
9.	Yellow in throat.	*C. Kotschyanus.*
	No yellow in throat.	*C. Kotschyanus* var. *leucopharynx*

C. Scharojanii was described by Ruprecht in Regel's *Gartenflora* in 1868 and named in honour of a Herr Scharojan who collected it in the Caucasus in August 1865. It has been found in but few localities in the Caucasus, originally near Mount Oschen, then on the Kroomdagh above Stauros near Trebizond, and again as lately as 1902 somewhere in the north-western Caucasus.

It is the only known autumn-flowering species with deep yellow flowers and has a very curious leaf in which the keel is as broad as the blade and so deeply grooved at the sides that it appears to be four-winged. This leaf structure is repeated in the closely related *C. vallicola*, also from the Caucasus, and in a less degree in *C. Kotschyanus*, but in no other species.

In *C. Scharojanii* the leaves appear later in spring than those of any other species, and make up for it by remaining green and active until the flowers appear, about the first week in August. That at least is what they should do when growing satisfactorily, and it is evident that they need more shade and cooler summer conditions than other Crocuses. In my own dry garden in spite of all efforts to provide a suitable situation the leaves turn brown in the hot weather of late June or July and disappear too soon. This may have been the cause of its dying out.

It makes a very small corm, always a bad sign and an indication of a species that relies more upon seed than root division for increase.

In the first edition of this book I wrote thus far in despairing fashion, little hoping to succeed in growing *C. Scharojanii*. Although it may be too late to help me, the rediscovery of the plant in marshy ground, by Mr. E. K. Balls, should encourage younger gardeners to start on fresh lines and treat it as a bog plant with high hopes of success. In his excellent article in the *Gardeners' Chronicle* of January 1936 he described finding it in Lazistan in such plenty that when seen from a distance the effect was like 'great golden stains on the wet slopes,' where they grew in 'myriads so closely together that the blooms pressed against one another.' His invaluable discovery that this Crocus flourishes in swampy ground in association with *Pinguicula vulgaris*, *Primula farinosa* and *Parnassia palustris* convinced him that it will certainly need considerably more moisture during the growing season and less drying out and ripening later than most other Crocus species. Then it seems likely that the bog garden or the banks of a stream will provide suitable conditions for successful cultivation. Mr. Balls found, as I had, that the corm is very small and very few had any offsets. Those that had ripened seeds had generally shrunk into a shrivelled knot, showing that propagation depends mostly upon seed.

The flowers are large with segments about two inches in length and of a fine orange yellow, generally with long, sharp points at their tips. The anthers are cream colour and the stigmata orange and slightly toothed at their edges.

It is so beautiful, standing up on its tube of three to four inches in height, that although it flowers so early in August when other flowers are plentiful it is worth growing whenever procurable.

C. vallicola was described by Herbert and is more widely distributed as a wild plant than the last, having been found in Armenia, Lazistan, Kurdistan, Georgia and the Caucasus. I always found it a delicate plant here, making no increase and soon dying out, but Maw speaks of it as easily cultivated and C. Wolley-Dod used to succeed well with it in his stiff clay soil near Malpas, Cheshire.

It is now very scarce in British gardens, and perhaps the only stock is that raised by Colonel Stern from seeds from the Tiflis Botanic Garden, which flower early in August in his paradise for sun-loving plants at Goring-by-Sea, Sussex.

The type form bears large creamy white flowers in mid-August. The segments are long for their width and terminate in a sharp point. They are veined internally with pale lilac and have two circular spots of bright yellow down in the throat.

Two varieties have been described. The first is var. *lilacinus*, a single plant of which was sent to Maw from Stauros, near Trebizond. It was smaller than the type and freely veined with lilac on both surfaces. There is a specimen of it in Maw's herbarium at the British Museum (Natural History), but all trace of lilac has faded out of it.

The second is the plant described by Carl Koch as *C. Suworowianus*, he having obtained it from Prince Konstantin Suvorov. Maw described it as a separate species, naming it *C. Zohrabii*, but afterwards in his monograph treated it as var. *Suwarrowianus* of *C. vallicola*, changing Koch's spelling of the

name. I have never seen a living specimen, so can only quote
Maw, who grew it from corms collected on the Palan-Ducken
range near Erzurum. He found that it flowered later than the
type and bore rounder flowers, with a beardless throat and
diphyllous proper spathes so short that, as also occurs in
C. Kotschyanus, they do not extend above the sheathing leaves.

Mr. John Hoog, of Haarlem, kindly sent me a flower and later
a plant of a very beautiful lemon yellow Crocus which he had
received from a lady residing at Kutais in the Caucasus.
Unfortunately my plant flowered and died. It was mostly like
C. Scharojanii var. *flavus* described by Lipsky.

C. cancellatus, described by Herbert in the *Botanical Magazine*
in the text to t. 3864 (1841), has no close affinity with any
other autumnal species. It lacks a basal spathe, has a coarsely
reticulated tunic and finely branched stigmata, and varies from
pure white to rich lilac, variously striped or feathered with
purple. The leaves are generally dormant when the flowers
appear, but sometimes push up a little before they fade, in
much the same way as those of *C. asturicus*. It has a wide range
from Greece to Persia, is found in Armenia and parts of
northern Asia Minor, and abundantly in Palestine and Syria,
where it is one of the species collected for food, and sold in the
markets of Damascus mixed with *C. aleppicus* under the name
of Hursinein.

In Greece it used to be plentiful on the Lycabettos and other
hills round Athens, and I had no difficulty in collecting it there
in spring by means of its conspicuously white-lined leaves. In
its western habitats the flower always has a white ground, but in
the Cilician Taurus and generally throughout Asia Minor the
ground colour is mostly lilac. It is a very variable plant, and
the Palestine forms include those with lilac or white ground
colour, and Post mentions a pink form, which I have not seen.

Few plants have had more names given to them than the
colour forms of this Crocus, but it is best to treat those described
as having a white ground as synonyms of the type, and those
with a lilac ground as the var. *Kotschianus*.

Thus *CC. Schimperi*, *Spruneri*, *dianthus*, *nudiflorus* of Sibthorp
and Smith, *margaritaceus* and *Mazziaricus* are white forms, and
pylarum, *damascenus*, var. *persicus*, *edulis* and Maw's var.

cilicicus are more or less lilac as to ground colour and included under Herbert's var. *Kotschianus*. The Greek forms are the earliest to flower in the garden; those from Palestine are the latest and consequently of but little use for outdoor cultivation. Its striped forms are easily recognised when in flower, being so much unlike any other leafless autumnal species, but in the case of almost white varieties one has to look for the much branched yellow stigmata and the coarsely reticulated tunic to make certain.

There is a very distinct plant listed as var. *cilicicus lilacinus* that might rank as a species should it be proved to come true from seed and to have a distinct geographical range, for it differs from the other forms of *C. cancellatus* in having white instead of yellow anthers, and long, narrow segments that are inclined to reflex in sunshine, in contrast with the wider segments and globose form of other varieties. It also flowers in September before the white forms, and is of a distinctly rosy hue of lilac with delicate, unbranched veinings of a slightly deeper shade.

C. medius of Balbis was so named as it was considered intermediate between *C. sativus* and *C. nudiflorus*. It is only found in the French Riviera, especially behind Mentone, in the Maritime Alps near Tenda, above San Remo and Alassio in Liguria, and as far south as Spezzia and eastward to Genoa.

It is a very handsome and hardy species, easily recognised in flower by its widely opening lilac blossoms marked in the throat with a radiating star of deep purple lines, only to be compared with those of some forms of *C. sativus*, which, however, differ in having well-developed leaves at the flowering time. Again the finely branched scarlet stigmata of *C. medius* are very conspicuous and distinct. It might be confused with *C. nudiflorus*, but that species lacks the purple star in the throat, and the coarsely reticulated tunic of *C. medius* would at once show it to be distinct.

In leaf, too, it is recognisable by its unusually conspicuous and wide, white central line. A fine white variety appeared in Mr. A. C. Bartholomew's garden at Reading. It retains the purple star in the throat which with the scarlet-fringed stigmata makes it very brilliant.

C. medius flowers here early in October when *C. speciosus* going over and is a valuable plant for a sunny border.

C. Kotschyanus of C. Koch is a name which the monographer Maw rejected in favour of *C. zonatus* of J. Gay, because the epithet had been used in 1846 by Herbert for a variety of *C. cancellatus*, and Koch's use of it for a species was not until 1853.

According to the present-day International Rules of Botanical Nomenclature it is permissible to use a name specifically if its use has been only in a varietal sense. This change of name is likely to be very unpopular among gardeners, who have been accustomed for such a long period to call this general favourite *C. zonatus*. Accompanying the excellent figure t. 9044 (1925) of the *Botanical Magazine* Dr. O. Stapf gave a detailed history of the use of these names by various authors.

C. Kotschyanus, although closely related to *C. vallicola* in its leaf structure, cream-coloured anthers, orange-spotted throat and closely veined segments, is as easy to grow as *C. vallicola* is difficult. Its rosy lilac, almost pink, flowers approach in colour those of some Colchicums, and, like them, generally appear early in September soon after the first heavy rains.

The corm is very peculiar, wider and flatter than those of other species, and never quite symmetrical in outline, having two or three slight protuberances on its outer edge. Its tunic is a very thin and shining membranous, and as the flowering shoot, encased in white sheathing scales, starts into growth by the end of July it is easy to recognise its corms at lifting time. It also has a peculiar method of increase, forming a quantity of small cormlets in clusters, I believe from the protuberances mentioned above. They are of the size and appearance of small grains of wheat, and so easily detached from the mother corm that they are difficult to collect in dry soil and therefore serve to spread this species into the stocks of others; and once in, it is a work of several seasons and much patience to clear the stocks again.

In some seasons, when the flowers push up suddenly after the first rains following a drought, they appear at first to be white, but after a day or two they change to the normal pink tone. This behaviour has now and then resulted in the listing of a white form that has more than once lightened my purse and undermined my faith in printed descriptions.

In September 1934 Mr. Peter R. Barr sent me a flower of a beautiful pure white variety, and in the following year he kindly sent me corms of this delightful addition to white autumnal Crocuses. The large orange spots in the throat are as bright as those of the ordinary form, and are even more conspicuous in the white flower.

The name *zonatus*, which we must now abandon, was so descriptive of the ring of the twelve golden spots, joined as a pair at the base of each segment, that I regret its displacement by the guttural, harsh-sounding substitute. *C. Kotschyanus* grows in mountainous localities in Cilicia and on Lebanon and Hermon; but is easily grown in any sunny border and is often the earliest Crocus to flower of the autumnal species.

C. Kotschyanus var. *leucopharynx* of B. L. Burtt is the new, and at present correct, name for the pretty Crocus that has been listed and grown in gardens for the last forty years as *C. karduchorum*, because under that name it was introduced by W. Siehe of Mersina, who collected it in Cilicia.

It differs much from the true *C. karduchorum* of Maw and so closely resembles typical *C. Kotschyanus* in structure that Mr. B. L. Burtt regards it as a colour variety and named it var. *leucopharynx* (which is 'white throat' in Greek) in an article in the *Gardener's Chronicle* of October 9th, 1948 (p. 118). From the gardener's point of view the two forms can be distinguished at a glance, because in an open flower of *leucopharynx* the white throat is very conspicuous and unlike that of any other autumnal Crocus, and also it begins to flower ten or more days later than the type.

If you try to match the ground colour with the R.H.S. Colour Chart by laying detached segments on the sheets you will find that there is very little difference between the two forms, and at different ages of the blossoms the paler shades of Heliotrope (sheet 82) or Violet (sheet 36) will agree with both.

However, when growing in the garden and the flowers are widely opened in the sunshine the general colour of the type seems to be a warm tint of rosy lilac, while that of the variety is a pale shade of bluish lavender.

The difference is due to the presence of large orange spots in the throat and the yellow stigmata of the type which reflect a warm rosy glow into the lilac ground colour, whereas in *leucopharynx* the absence of yellow colouring and the large surface of white which covers the lowest third of all the segments produce a cold reflection of clear light without colour.

The variety has rather larger flowers, in which the segments are not rounded at the apex but, especially in the three outer ones, terminate in a short mucro; the veins are more distinct and bluer than the ground colour, and the anthers and stigmata are of a very pale cream colour.

When we first obtained it, I and many others found it difficult to establish, chiefly owing to a very peculiar habit which caused the flowering shoot to grow horizontally underground instead of straight upwards. Unless the soil was removed and the corm and shoot were tilted upwards it failed to reach the light and flowers and leaves rotted. Those that survived long enough to produce the characteristic small cormlets provided an easy method of propagation. If collected and potted, as we should do in the rather similar 'spawn' bulblets of *Iris histrioides*, they grow to flowering size in two seasons.

If these cormlets are plentifully produced it is very difficult to collect all of them as they are generally detached from the mother corm by lifting time, and some are no larger than the so-called 'ants' eggs.' Those that are missed and dug in reappear after a season or two as flowering corms. Here they are now 'gatecrashers' in the Crocus beds and as difficult to rogue out of other stocks as those arch-intruders *CC. speciosus* and *Tomasinianus*.

I find it a good plan when lifting var. *leucopharynx* to delay replanting until the flowering shoots have grown long enough to show in which direction they intend to proceed. They mostly lie flat along the upper side of the remarkably flattened corm, and all goes well if the corm is tilted so that the shoot may continue its growth upwards.

I believe that when this Crocus is vigorous it will form two new corms from two of the irregular knobs on opposite margins of the old one and that these are tilted at opposite angles like the two sides of a double-sided roof.

If left undisturbed in this position both flowering shoots

would grow pressed along the surface of each corm towards its upper margin, and thus both would reach the surface.

In *C. Kotschyanus* and the var. *leucopharynx* the sheathing leaves are so long that the two uppermost enclose the monophyllous proper spathe, a peculiar character only found in *CC. vallicola* var. *Suwarrowianus* and *Autranii*.

Two species deserve mention here, viz. *C. Autranii* and the true *C. karduchorum,* because they are in some ways allied to *C. Kotschyanus,* and though neither is at present in cultivation they would provide interesting and desirable plant quests for collectors.

C. Autranii was described by Alboff in the *Bulletin de l'Herbier Boissier* in 1893 from specimens collected in Abkhazia, Transcaucasia, in alpine pastures on Mount Czipshira at an altitude of 7,000 feet and named in honour of a Swiss botanist, Eugène J. B. Autran (1855-1912).

Herr Max Leichtlin, shortly before his death, kindly sent me his only corm of this rare species, and I much regret that I was never successful in flowering it before it eventually died. I therefore only know it from examining some of the specimens kindly lent to the British Museum (Natural History) for that purpose by the curator of the Boissier Herbarium at Geneva, who also presented one specimen to the British Museum Herbarium.

This examination revealed the presence of a basal spathe, which was not mentioned in the original description.

C. Autranii differs from *C. Kotschyanus* in its deeper purple flowers, the absence of yellow spots in the glabrous throat, its white instead of orange filaments and bright orange stigmata, and a much smaller round corm with fewer fibres in the membranous tunic.

The plant described and figured by Maw as *C. karduchorum* was discovered by Theodor Kotschy south of Lake Van in Kurdistan in 1859, and specimens were distributed to many European herbaria. When Maw published his monograph in 1886 it had not been in cultivation, so the plate V was drawn from dried material at Vienna.

It represents a plant unlike any other Crocus in its very short and narrow leaves, which had persisted through the summer until the autumnal flowering period and were still green, while dissection showed a second set of leaves surrounding the ovary about half an inch in length.

It is possible that these dormant leaves developed thus far during the gradual drying of the corm, but this does not explain the presence of such feeble leaves, only one-twentieth of an inch wide and not more than two inches long, which would seem too frail to be of use for the nourishment of the growing plant to warrant their retention until the flowering period. *CC. Scharojanii* and *byzantinus*, which produce their leaves late and retain them longer than other Croci, have wide leaves ten to twelve inches in length.

In *The Garden* for September 25th, 1886, Maw recorded the flowering of corms of *C. karduchorum* sent to him by an American missionary from Siwas in Asia Minor.

There is no mention of the leaves, most likely because they had perished in transit. He describes the flowers as a little bluer in tint than in his illustration, with about nine fine purple lines, extending half-way up the segments which were not visible in the faded dry specimens. *C. karduchorum* somewhat resembles *C. zonatus* of Gay, but the flowers are smaller, and instead of the bright golden zone at the base of the inner surface of the segments above its throat two small orange spots occur similar to those of *C. vallicola* of Herbert.

These small spots and the bluish tint seem to connect *C. karduchorum* more closely with the var. *leucopharynx* than with the typical *C. Kotschyanus*.

In September 1928 Mr. Peter R. Barr sent me a specimen from a stock he had received in the preceding year from Siehe as *C. karduchorum*, of which he wrote the two small yellow spots at base of segments are very conspicuous.

I have found a few similarly marked blooms among *leucopharynx* here, and have wondered whether they were from seed perhaps pollinated by the type.

C. byzantinus of Ker is best known by the name *C. iridiflorus* of Heuffel.

The *Index Kewensis*, however, selects the older name of *C. byzantinus*, used by Clusius and Parkinson, because Ker adopts it, in combination with these early descriptions in the *Botanical Magazine* for 1808, under t. 1111, and this constitutes the first valid publication of the name. We should therefore use the less truthful name *C. byzantinus* instead of the later *C. iridiflorus* which was published in Reichenbach's *Icones Florae Germanicae* in 1847. Although the systematic botanist should obey the rules and use the oldest valid name the gardener may be forgiven for using '*iridiflorus*,' the name chosen by Maw.

It is found in Hungary and Transylvania and not, as the epithet *byzantinus* would imply, near Constantinople. It is the only known species in which the outer segments are twice as long as the inner; they are frequently of a rich purple, while the inner may be nearly white. When fully expanded the outer segments often reflex, while the smaller, inner ones stand stiffly upright and then the flower looks more like an Iris than a Crocus. From this peculiarity it has been placed in a separate genus by Schur under the name of *Crociris iridiflora*. The outer segments are two inches or more in length and one in width, but the inner are narrow and pointed, about an inch long and half an inch wide, generally much paler than the outer and veined with purple. It differs also from all other Crocuses in having light purple stigmata divided into narrow feathery threads. It has been noticed that the anthers differ from those of other species in being *introrse*, that is their valves open on the inner side so that the pollen is massed close up to the style. In all other Crocuses that I have examined the anthers are *extrorse*, opening on their outer side, towards the inner surface of the outer segments on which they are fixed.

As yet I have not been able to examine a sufficient number of specimens to be certain that the anthers are invariably introrse.

There is a form in which the stigmatic threads are white and also a variety with pure white segments and pale yellow stigmata. The late Mr. Allen, of Shepton Mallet, who enriched gardens with many beautiful seedlings of Snowdrops and Scillas, also raised some fine varieties of this Crocus. One named 'President' was very large and deep purple, 'Rosamond' of a uniform pale lilac, and 'Ruby,' as the name suggests, of a good red-purple.

It is not often seen in gardens, but is a robust and easily grown plant if it be remembered that it is a native of woods and evidently requires more shade and moisture than other species. I find it thrives in soil that is chiefly peat or leaf mould in the position one would choose for a choice Hellebore or fern, that is on the northern or north-western side of a boulder in the rock garden or under some small deciduous shrub. It has peculiarly broad leaves, slightly glaucous on the under side, but of a uniform deep green above, and without the central stripe of white that is so characteristic of most other species of Crocus. This breadth and dark colouring point to its preference for a shady situation.

C. speciosus of Bieberstein is widely spread in eastern Europe and Asia Minor, being found in the Crimea, the Caucasus and Armenia and extending as far east as north-east Persia.

It naturally follows that it should be variable, but best of all it is beautiful and hardy as well as plentiful. Left to go its own way it will spread freely in borders and even under deciduous shrubs, and then provides carpets and mimic pools of blue in September as rich as those of bluebells in May.

The corm is large and round, covered by a thin papery membrane, with conspicuous rings in the lowest third, and if lifted when dormant in July or August will generally be found with a longer and whiter shoot growing from its summit than in any other species except *C. Kotschyanus*. Though so distinct in corm tunic and other characters these two species increase rapidly by small cormlets. These are formed round the base of the corm in the case of *C. speciosus*, and a dozen or more may be found on a large corm. They are very slightly attached when dormant, and so difficult to collect when dropped into the soil that it is wise not to grow *C. speciosus* near other annulate species if clean stocks are wanted. In a flower border this does not matter and helps to spread the drifts of this glorious Crocus, certainly the finest of all autumnal species.

The large flowers shoot up as though by magic a day or so after the tips of the white scale leaves pierce through the soil, and are of a peculiar blue tint of lilac which is made to appear even bluer at a little distance by the fine veinings of the inner surface of all the segments. These markings are peculiar to this species, for a great number of fine, blue lines start out of the central vein and extend to the margins, and, especially in the inner segments, appear to pass without a break behind the two secondary veins. The outer surface of the lower portion of the flower is generally marked with dark blue dots, so that either closed or open the general effect is bluer than in most Crocuses. The stigmata are very large and showy, divided into a mass of orange-scarlet threads, wonderfully conspicuous against the lilac and blue. The anthers are yellow, a character that at once distinguishes it from the closely related *C. pulchellus*.

A pure white variety was found by Mr. Van Tubergen among plants of a large and pale-flowered form collected near Schemacha and I have raised other white forms, not quite so pure, but perhaps all the more beautiful on account of a faint flush of lilac on newly opened flowers, and the presence of the characteristic veinings in a pale tint of bluish-lilac. A smaller and later-flowering form with an extra amount of blue in it was at one time listed as var. *globosus* and is useful in carrying on the flowering season until November.

The largest-flowered autumnal Crocus is a form of *C. speciosus* known as var. *Aitchisonii*, in which the outer segments are three inches or more in length. It is paler than the typical form and less veined, of a pale uniform shade of lavender within, and almost white outside when in bud, and does not flower before mid-October. 'Artabir,' 'Cassiope' and 'Pollux' are forms of *C. speciosus* selected by Messrs. Van Tubergen out of importations from the Caucasus.

Hybrids occur fairly frequently where *C. speciosus* and *C. pulchellus* are grown as neighbours, especially if the late-flowering form *globosus* is there. They mostly resemble *C. speciosus*, and show their *pulchellus* parentage in white or cream-coloured anthers and the presence of a certain amount of yellow in the throat, which is normally white in forms of *C. speciosus*.

C. pulchellus in its blue and white forms was described by Herbert in 1841. It grows in Turkey near Constantinople, on

D

Mount Olympus above Bursa (Brusa), in the hills behind
Salonica and on Mount Athos.

It is nearly related to *C. speciosus* but has a thicker, harder
corm tunic, forms a smaller corm, flowers a fortnight later, and
is very different in colour. The anthers are white, the stigmata
yellow or orange, the throat orange; the pale lavender segments
lack the parallel cross veining of *C. speciosus* and are only
marked with five slightly branched bluish veins. The filaments
are yellow and covered with fine hairs in *C. pulchellus* but white
and glabrous in *C. speciosus*. It grows well in the open border
but does not increase so rapidly as *C. speciosus*. As the white
form is of good substance it is one of the most beautiful of early
autumnal albino forms.

Three imperfectly known species are inserted here, though
for want of fuller knowledge I have not included them in the
key at the head of this chapter.

C. hermoneus of Kotschy was gathered among melting snow
near the summit of Mount Hermon but in a fruiting state only.
According to Post the leaves appear after the flowers, which
are white with stigmata dissected into few threadlike lobes and
appear in October. Plants collected for it in Palestine had
finely reticulated tunics instead of the thin membranous one of
the original specimens and in Post's description. They bore
thin, starry flowers, mostly tinged with lilac and looked like
poor forms of *C. cancellatus*, and I think we have not yet received
Kotschy's plant. These others were delicate in constitution and
soon died out here even in the cold frame.

C. moabiticus of Bornmüller and Dinsmore was first described
in 1912. It was collected by Mr. J. E. Dinsmore, of Jerusalem,
at Zizeh in the plain of Moab, flowering in November without
leaves. The flowers are small and white with purple stripes, or
tinted with light violet. The anthers are yellow and the long,
nearly entire stigmata of deep orange are about as long as the
segments. It has a basal spathe, diphyllous proper spathes,
numerous and narrow leaves generally with glabrous edges, but
occasionally armed with a few scattered teeth. It has not been
introduced to cultivation.

From another district of Transjordan some corms were
collected as *C. cancellatus* var. *damascenus*. They flowered here last

autumn and differ from *C. moabiticus* in having long leaves at flowering time in October, with ciliated margins to both blade and keel. The flowers were small and squat, dull white with lilac stripes, and unless they improve with cultivation will be more interesting than beautiful. It is not fair to judge from one season's trial, as unfortunately they died without justifying any claim for praise.

V

Autumnal Species Flowering with Leaves

THE autumnal Crocuses that have well-developed leaves at their flowering time can be divided into two groups.

1. Those with ciliated margins to the blades and keel of the leaf, which form the *sativus* group dealt with in Chapter VI.

2. Those with smooth, generally termed glabrous, leaves.

Of these last *CC. Clusii, Salzmannii* and *serotinus* have been included in Chapter III, leaving ten species for this chapter. Six of these, viz. *CC. caspius, Boryi, Tournefortii, Veneris, hyemalis* and *laevigatus* are closely connected by their Eastern range and membranous tunics. The others differ widely in structure and habitat.

An artificial key to autumnal species with glabrous leaves produced before the flowers may be arranged thus:

1.	Flowers banded or striped externally.	2.
	Flowers not banded or striped externally.	5.
2.	Flowers large.	3.
	Flowers very small.	4.
3.	Anthers black or yellow.	*C. hyemalis.*
	Anthers white.	*C. lævigatus.*
4.	Stigmata overtopping anthers.	*C. Veneris.*
	Stigmata shorter than anthers.	*C. Gaillardotii.*
5.	Flowers lilac.	6.
	Flowers white.	9.
6.	Anthers yellow.	7.
	Anthers white.	*C. Tournefortii.*
7.	Throat white.	*C. Clusii.*
	Throat not white.	8.
8.	Throat yellowish.	*C. Salzmannii.*
	Throat orange.	*C. longiflorus.*
9.	Anthers yellow.	10.
	Anthers white.	11.

10. $\left\{\begin{array}{l}\text{Stigmata scarlet.}\\ \text{Stigmata yellow.}\end{array}\right.$ *C. niveus.*
C. caspius.

11. $\left\{\begin{array}{l}\text{Stigmata finely divided.}\\ \text{Stigmata entire (more or less).}\end{array}\right.$ *C. Boryi.*
C. ochroleucus.

C. longiflorus of Rafinesque is unfortunately the correct name by the law of priority for this remarkably fragrant species more happily named *C. odorus* by Bivona Bernardi. Its scent resembles that of primroses or of *Iris unguicularis* and is so strong that a few blossoms will scent a room. The only Crocuses that can rival it in fragrance are *CC. laevigatus* in winter and *Imperati* and *suaveolens* in early spring. Moreover the flowers are not remarkable for their length but are generally rather globose with well-rounded segments.

The monophyllous proper spathe is green and leaf-like in its upper portion, a character which, taken together with the scarlet, more or less divided stigmata and the orange throat and anthers should easily distinguish *C. longiflorus* from other lilac autumn-flowering species. It flowers in October and into November and is very hardy and reliable in the open border, although a native of southern Italy, Sicily and Malta. The tunic is coarsely netted and the nearly spherical corm about three-quarters of an inch in diameter.

The flowers vary a great deal in colour but I have only once seen a white form. Pale lavender forms, with or without external purple featherings, frequently occur among my seedlings and encourage me to hope for a true albino some day. The typical form is a uniform lilac with a good deal of pink in it, but not so rosy as *C. Kotschyanus*. The variety *melitensis* occurs in Malta and varies as to the purple external markings of all six segments. They may appear as basal lines only, or as branched featherings reaching to the tips of the segments, or again as cloudy blotches on the lower halves. I obtained a few corms in 1895, which I believe came from the Berlin Botanic Gardens, as var. *Wilhelmii*, which differ from the type by a paler ground colour, less regular outline and thinner texture. When crossed with the var. *melitensis* they have given some particularly pleasing seedlings. One of these which I gave to Mr. Herbert Chapman, of Rye, makes a very beautiful pot plant for the Alpine House, and when shown at Vincent Square as grown in a cold house received an Award of Merit in 1921 under the name of var. *venustus*.

C. Tournefortii was named by J. Gay in honour of the great French botanist Joseph Pitton de Tournefort (1656-1708). It is only found in the islands of the Greek Archipelago. It has the reputation of being somewhat tender, but I have found it easily grown here in well-drained soil where it can receive all the sunshine available in October and November when it flowers. It makes very large corms of an inch or more in diameter, which, in size and in the soft membranous tunic, closely resemble those of *C. Salzmannii*. Like other species with large corms it increases rapidly by division and requires frequent replanting to prevent it becoming crowded and impoverished.

The flowers are very beautiful and in colour quite unlike those of any other species. Maw's figure does not do it justice in form or colour and looks as though drawn from a dried specimen. Fitch's plate—t. 5776 (1869) of the *Botanical Magazine*, under the name of *C. Orphanidis*—gives a better idea of it but misses the charm of the white anthers. The colour is difficult to describe tersely; it is a warm rosy lilac, with something of a pastelle or body colour effect about it, very different for instance from the clear transparent lilac of *C. pulchellus*. The inner surface of the flower is of a wonderfully uniform tint, being very slightly veined, and the bright scarlet, finely branched stigmata, white anthers and bright yellow throat give a wonderful finish to its charm. Once flowers open they refuse to close again, even more resolutely than those of some forms of *C. sativus*. Flowering so late in the season they frequently suffer from the effects of rain unless protected overhead. This habit possibly works satisfactorily enough in its native home, and is a hint to us that a cruise among those wonderful islands would be blest by an autumnal repetition of halcyon days during the flowering season of this lovely Crocus.

Seedlings have shown very little tendency to vary, pale forms and one with fine bluish featherings are interesting but no improvement on their really perfect parent.

C. niveus of Bowles was described as *C. marathonisius* in 1876 and distributed as herbarium specimens by Professor Heldreich, of the Athens Botanical Gardens. Unfortunately the description is misleading in some points and the specimens are mixed, some forms of the really very distinct *C. Boryi* being included.

This led Maw to rank the plant as a variety of *C. Boryi* under the name var. *marathoniseus*, spelt thus with an 'e.' However, it was first gathered at Marathonisi, the ancient Gytheion in Laconia, and so the spelling should be *marathonisius*.

I redescribed it as a new species in the *Gardeners' Chronicle* for November 10th, 1900, under the name of *C. niveus*, because Heldreich's description is incorrect as to the corm tunic, which he must have described from that of *C. Boryi* as subcoriaceous and striate, whereas it is distinctly reticulated in *C. niveus*.

The presence of a basal spathe is not referred to by Heldreich, which again agrees with *C. Boryi*, and not with *C. niveus*. So it is a difficult question to decide what the correct name is. The late James Britten told me Heldreich's name should stand, and I published a note to that effect in the *Gardeners' Chronicle*, January 19th, 1901, but the late J. G. Baker often told me I ought to stick to *niveus*, as it occurs in the first complete and correct description published, and I therefore restore it here.

Mr. B. L. Burtt has recently investigated the question as to the validity of the name *C. niveus* in an article published in the *Gardeners' Chronicle*, October 23rd, 1948, p. 134. Here he states that examination of the specimens collected by Fontenay, which are cited by Heldreich as types of *C. marathonisius*, shows that some had white anthers and are therefore a form of *C. Boryi*, and that Heldreich's name of *marathonisius* covers two distinct Crocuses.

Mr. Burtt decides that as the 'type method' is now incorporated in the International Rules of Botanical Nomenclature it is right to reject the name *marathonisius* on the grounds that it is based on a mixture of two species and is a '*nomen confusum.*'

Thus he concludes that *C. niveus* Bowles is valid for the plant with yellow anthers, and *C. marathonisius* of Heldreich with white anthers becomes a synonym of *C. Boryi* J. Gay.

Anyway it is far and away the most beautiful of all white-flowered autumnal species, with flowers two inches or more in length, a rich orange throat and bright scarlet stigmata which make the purity of its whiteness the more dazzling. It has yellow anthers and green-veined, diphyllous proper spathes, and in all of its characters, except the diphyllous proper spathe, is more closely related to *C. longiflorus* than to *C. Boryi*, with which it has been confused. I find it a very hardy and robust plant which seeds freely, but flowers so late in the year—sometimes not before the end of November, and even into January—that it deserves the protection of a handlight at its flowering time. It has also been found on Mount Taygetus and Heldreich records it from Leucadia. It is figured in *Bot. Mag.*, n.s., t. 146.

C. caspius of Fischer and Meyer is a comparatively recent introduction to English gardens. It was discovered by Hohenacker in 1838 on the western and southern shores of the Caspian Sea, but efforts to introduce it failed until C. J. Van Tubergen, of Haarlem, employed a collector to obtain it in 1902. He succeeded in finding it in Russian Talish, south-west of the Caspian, south of Baku. Though coming from such a southern home and growing no higher than 1,000 feet above sea level under the shelter of low bushes, it has proved perfectly hardy and blossoms freely in the open ground.

At first the plants flowered over a long period from October to February, but as they settled down they gradually became more regular and now make a good show in mid-October. It has a very smooth membranous tunic of a rosy hue of brown, a corm about the size of a hazel nut, diphyllous proper spathes, well-shaped, globular, white flowers with rich orange throat, yellow anthers and orange undivided stigmata.

A few of the collected corms were of a rosy lilac tint and the most pronounced of these I described as var. *lilacinus* (but misprinted as *Lillaceus*) in the *Gardeners' Chronicle*, November 21st, 1903. The white form is the more beautiful.

C. Boryi of J. Gay is widely distributed in Greece, on the mainland and in the islands, and Corfu. I have collected it close to the shore in the Bay of Phaleron, and high in the hills near Tripolis growing among *CC. chrysanthus* and *Crewei*. From these it is easily distinguished in March by the very narrow leaves in which the central white stripe is very conspicuous and covers more than half of the width of the upper surface. They are also remarkably long, measuring up to eighteen inches in length at maturity and as many as seven in number.

The flowers though small are exquisitely beautiful, not quite white but lightly flushed with a pale sulphur tint which shows up the white anthers very pleasingly, and the finely divided stigmata are bright scarlet and very conspicuous. It is unfortunately rather tender and misses the autumnal sunshine of its southern home, but is a gem for a cold frame or Alpine house. There is a variety of it with lilac featherings but it is not so beautiful as the white form.

C. ochroleucus of Boissier approaches most nearly to the group of Spanish species in structure but is only found in Syria, in very rocky places on the Phœnician coast, on Lebanon and Anti-Lebanon and in Galilee. Maw's figure is larger and handsomer than any form I have seen in cultivation, and as he by no means flattered the flowers of other species one is led to hope that there may yet arrive a form to equal the figure.

It is a very hardy free-growing plant, making an abundance of small cormlets every season from many points on the surface of the old corm. If dug in deeply these youngsters appear to remain as vigorous as those more carefully planted. The corm is wide and flat, with a tunic of parallel fibres on a thin membranous base. It begins to flower after most other autumnal species, except *C. laevigatus*, are over, and therefore is a valuable though perhaps not very showy species. The first flowers to appear generally do so before their leaves, but the second flower from each shoot is accompanied by the rapidly developing leaves. The flowers are not quite white, being slightly tinged with cream colour. In some the throat is very faintly stained with orange, in others it is brighter. The narrow segments, not much more than an inch long, are veined with lines that appear grey, more from being transparent than from containing any pigment. The white anthers distinguish *C. ochroleucus* from any albino form of the Spanish group, and the short' leaves and yellow stigmata, generally very little divided, prevent its confusion with other white Eastern species. Post mentions a lilac form, but I have never seen it.

C. laevigatus of Bory de St. Vincent is unique as to its corm tunic, which is hard and smooth, almost woody, and formed of one piece only which entirely covers the corm, splitting at the base into vandyked points that permit the roots to push out between them. So hard a substance decays slowly, and many

layers of tunics may be found superimposed and pushed
upwards by the growing corm. I collected some near Athens
that showed remains of fifteen tunics, the product of as many
years. The old ones become dull and leathery, but when
cleaned away that of the last season's growth is so smooth that
it resembles the shell of a hazel nut. If gently rubbed an outer
skin may be removed, and the tunic when quite dry is then of a
peculiar light drab colour. This tunic is even more highly
polished on its inner surface and its smoothness has provided
the name of *laevigatus*, from the Latin *levis*=smooth. It is widely
distributed in Greece, the Morea and the Cyclades, and is a
very variable species. All those I collected had a white ground
colour, mostly veined and feathered with crimson-purple on
the outer segments. A few were pure white except for the
orange throat and a band of soft butter-yellow on the outer
surface of the three outer segments. Max Leichtlin sent me a
large flowered form which I call var. *major* in which the ground
colour is flushed with a very delicate lilac, and there are purple
lines on the outer segments. Seedlings from this vary slightly in
the amount of purple markings but remain a distinct race. He
also sent me as *C. Fontenayi* of Heldreich a very beautiful form
with bright rosy lilac ground and buff exterior, so richly
feathered that it looks very much like a small form of the totally
different plant *C. Imperati*. It differs from the typical *C. laevigatus*
not only in its larger and more richly coloured flowers but also
by flowering in December and onwards, whereas the white
grounded forms commence flowering in October. It therefore
seems best to call it *C. laevigatus* var. *Fontenayi*. It seeds freely
and seedlings retain its distinguishing characters.

The figure in the *Botanical Magazine*, t. 9515 (1938), was
drawn from specimens from my garden.

It clearly shows the wide, rounded segments of this
uncommon and very superior form.

C. laevigatus is one of the most fragrant species and would be
excellent for a cold house, and is also so hardy that in spite of
flowering so late in the season it is a great ornament in sheltered
nooks of the rock garden. Its white anthers and finely divided
stigmata are much like those of *C. Boryi*, but its lilac or richly
feathered flowers easily distinguish it. In its albino form,

however, the curious corm tunic can be relied upon as the final court of appeal.

This unique type of tunic provides an extremely useful method of dividing different forms of Crocuses with corm tunics so similar that a stray from a neighbouring stock would pass unnoticed at lifting time. This has been a frequent source of confusion, especially among species and varieties with annulate tunics. By planting a row of some form of *C. laevigatus* between two kinds with indistinguishable tunics I obtain unfailing evidence that on the opposite sides of my *laevigatus* row the corms are to be kept separate.

By planting reticulate species alternately with parallel or annulate one a similar end is achieved. I never have enough reticulates for the purpose so I use rows of *laevigatus*, and their flowers are very welcome throughout the winter.

C. cretensis of Körnicke is included by Mr. Burtt in his contribution to Rechinger's *Florae Aegaeae Supplementum* in *Phyton*, Vol. I, p. 223 (1949).

It has been collected recently in Crete by Mr. Peter Davis. Formerly it has been confused with *C. Veneris*, which is endemic to Cyprus and has a very different fibrous corm tunic, whereas the Cretan plant has a hard shining tunic resembling that of *C. laevigatus*, said not to split into triangular segments at the base. It would be interesting to learn how the young roots escape from such an entire tunic.

*C. hyemalis** of Boissier and Blanche is a species peculiar to Palestine and Syria and is plentiful near Jerusalem, Jericho and Bethlehem, at Aintab and Damascus.

As it comes from so far south and flowers in mid-winter it is best grown in a frame, and I have never been able to keep it in health for many seasons out in the open, but in the upper, and therefore drier, part of a cold frame it ripened and flowered well for many years. It grows plentifully in the Camp di Pastori near Bethlehem, and I like to think that the shepherds of Bethlehem listened to the first Christmas carol while resting on a field full of the flowers of *C. hyemalis*. The white, starry flowers are deep orange in the throat and vary

* Photographs of the wild plant by Mrs. R. McConnel have appeared in *Bull. Alpine Garden Soc. 10*, 137, 139 (1942).

much as to the amount of purple spots or featherings on the outer segments.

The anthers of the typical form are described by Maw as orange and by Dr. Post as brownish. In the var. *Foxii* of Maw from the neighbourhood of Jericho they are black, and this was the only form known in cultivation, and all my efforts to obtain the others proved fruitless until Mrs. McConnel sent me corms which she found near Athlit.

These have yellow anthers but such narrow and pointed segments that they are more interesting than beautiful.

A single corm of a very beautiful and extraordinary Crocus was sent to me in 1918, which at a first glance seemed to be a form of *C. hyemalis*, but closer examination showed that it had white anthers and a stiff hard corm tunic, in which character it resembled *C. laevigatus*.

It had been obtained from Verter & Co., the American Colony Stores, Jerusalem, who used to collect and sell very good and rare local plants.

It was sent as *C. Gaillardotii*, so it may have been collected growing among that very different species in Syria.

I made a drawing and a description of it and dried a flower, and regret that these are all I now possess of what I believe to be an undescribed species. The drawing shows eight leaves and six flowers from one of the two flowering shoots.

The flowers were white with segments one and a quarter inches long by three-eighths of an inch wide. The outer segments had three stripes on the back, the central one dark blue, not purple, reaching more than half the length of the segments. The stigmatic branches divided into numerous slender threads, bright orange in colour. It is possible that corms of this charming Crocus are frequently roasted for food in Damascus along with those of *C. Gaillardotii* instead of being picked out to be sold to gardeners. They should be easily recognised among the others by the smooth, stiff corm tunic.

C. Veneris is a diminutive species only distinguishable from *C. Boryi* by its being half the size. It only occurs in Crete and Cyprus. I have seen living specimens grown by H. J. Elwes at Colesbourne, but it is not often seen in cultivation.

C. aleppicus of Baker is another Syrian species not in

general cultivation, although it is said to be so plentiful round Damascus that the roots are gathered for food and sold cheaply in the market. It is the *C. Gaillardotii* of Maw and perhaps *C. intromissus* of Herbert. It has a finely reticulated tunic, according to Maw and Herbert, but Post describes it as of parallel fibres.

It must be an interesting species, with very small white flowers variously marked externally with pale lilac, divided stigmata shorter than the white anthers, and leaves that curl inward. The corm, too, should have a cap of curiously long chaffy points projecting above the tunic. It flowers in mid-winter and with such remarkable characters should be easily recognised and collected.

The few plants I was able to obtain only flowered once and failed to survive.

VI

The Saffron Crocus

CROCUS SATIVUS of Linnæus is the Crocus of the ancient world, having been cultivated and prized from a remote period for the sake of its scented stigmata, which after careful drying provide the drug Saffron.

It has been, and still is, cultivated from Spain to Kashmir, was once largely grown in England at Saffron Walden, and has been grown as a crop in some parts of America.

It is supposed to be the Karkom of the Song of Solomon, which is Kurkuma in Sanscrit and Kurkum in Indian languages. Thus the consonants K R K represent the root word in ancient Eastern tongues. When Phœnician merchants carried this precious drug about the world, nations speaking different languages would no doubt adopt the form of the name but alter the vowel sounds. Crocum is a form used by Clusius and some Latin writers, and the Greeks turned it into Κροχος. This in its latinised form Crocus is our present-day name for the plant, though we use the Arabic word Zà-ferán, anglicised into Saffron, for the drug. Thus Crocus, with plural Crocuses, has become the familiar English name for the plant, and surely must be one of the oldest flower names in such common use, for although we have lengthened the sound of the first syllable to that of omega instead of omikron it is still the same word.

The drug was renowned for its medicinal powers, perfume and flavour, and as a brilliant yellow dye, and was always very costly. This is not strange, if it is true, as Pereira states, that one grain of good Saffron contains the stigmata of nine flowers, so that one ounce would represent the produce of four thousand three hundred and twenty flowers. It is moreover not an easy plant to cultivate, being liable to attacks from parasitic fungi. Many of these outbreaks have been carefully investigated and form the subjects of publications. Again, both the flowers and the plants themselves are easily damaged by rough weather.

So the high price it has commanded has always led to the invention of ingenious ways of adulterating it. Even in the days of Dioscorides and Pliny it was moistened, mixed with fat, or otherwise tampered with, and the latter tells us 'Nothing is so subject to sophistication as Saffron and therefore the only trial of true Saffron is this, if a man lay his hands upon it, he shall heare it to cracke as if it were brittle and readie to burst: for that which is moist (a qualitie coming of some indirect means and cunning cast) yieldeth to the hand and makes no words.'

During the Middle Ages severe laws were enacted against the adulteration of Saffron. The Saffron Inspectors of Nuremberg caused one Jobst Findeker to be burnt in the same fire as his adulterated Saffron in 1444, while in 1456 two men and a woman were buried alive for a like offence.

In later times the dried flowers of Safflower (*Carthamus tinctorius*) have been used instead of Saffron, or mixed with it, without risk of penalty.

Yet it appears to have been a lucrative crop when well managed, and growers on the lower spurs of the Apennines have in some seasons made such profits that one year's harvest has exceeded the value of the land under cultivation.

The account of the Saffron industry at Saffron Walden as given in Miller's *Gardener's Dictionary* (1768) is worth reading. He gives a table of charges and profits that show, at the price of thirty shillings a pound for Saffron, the net profits of an acre were then about five pounds four shillings a year, without counting any return for the sale of surplus roots.

The industry has long since ceased in England, and now the greatest Saffron producing country is Spain. Flückiger and Hanbury give figures of the exports from Spain, and state that in 1870 43,950 lb. were imported into the United Kingdom, valued at £95,690.

Saffron is no longer used medicinally and retains a place in the pharmacopœia solely for its value as a colouring agent, although otherwise superseded as a dye by less costly substances.

In Cornwall it is still much used for flavouring Saffron cakes. The great increase in numbers of summer trippers has brought about a curious change and deterioration of these dainties as

sold by pastrycooks in the towns. The visitors thought it the
right thing to eat these bright yellow cakes and buns, but found
that though they admired the colour they disliked the flavour
and only bought one. So now a special brand is baked for
visitors who have not acquired the taste for real Saffron, but
are pleased with the colouring produced by turmeric or
Safflower or some synthetic aniline dye.

Things were different in the year 1670 when Johann
Ferdinand Hertodt published at Jena his *Crocologia*, a duodecimo volume of nearly three hundred pages, to set forth the
virtues of Saffron as a panacea. There was no disease known
then that he did not profess to cure by a prescription in which
Saffron was one of the ingredients. If one could but believe him,
the Plague, melancholia, bites of venomous beasts, toothache or
madness would yield to a treatment of Saffron. Many strange
substances, such as worm-eaten wood of oaks, the fat of the
mountain mouse, swallows' nests and dragon's blood, myrrh
and aloes, henbane and opium and other powerful drugs, are
included in his draughts and ointments, but it is always
Saffron that is the leading feature of the cure. It is even
recommended as a dye for hair, should one desire it of a brilliant
yellow, but the chemical blonde of the present day would
no doubt consider peroxide of hydrogen a more certain agent.

Linnæus seems to have been so much impressed with the
importance of the Saffron-producing Crocus that he regarded
all others as mere varieties of it—and yet long before his date
the cultivated plant had become a sterile variety that could
only be propagated by root division and was nowhere to be
found as a wild plant.

Like so many of our domesticated plants, for instance Maize,
the Potato and the Florentine Iris, its origin is uncertain. The
most nearly related form is one described by Parlatore as
C. Orsinii. It only differs from the cultivated plant in the length
of its stigmata, which do not hang out of the flower in the
manner peculiar to the Saffron Crocus. It has only been
recorded from three localities in the neighbourhood of Ascoli,
in Italy, and though they are apparently in wild country it is
not impossible that roots of the cultivated form might have
been conveyed there from crops grown in that district.

The smaller-flowered form common around Athens and in other parts of Greece and the Cyclades, known as var. *Cartwrightianus*, seems to be a possible parent of the officinal plant. It has the same habit as the cultivated Saffron Crocus of remaining open at night and in bad weather, and has the stigmata so disproportionate in comparison with the size of the segments that they protrude between them. I collected it many years ago on Lycabettos and again in 1938, and though not in flower at the time I found great variation in size and colour among those I brought home. Some of them are much like the Saffron Crocus in colour and markings, and make corms as large.

It seems to me quite possible that if this plant were grown largely for the sake of its long, red stigmata, and those seedlings producing the longest were selected, it need not be many years before some form much like the cultivated Saffron Crocus could be found.

Many botanists regard several forms very distinct in appearance as no more than varieties of *C. sativus*. They are so variable that it is difficult to fix exact limitations, and the following key is not infallible:

The sativus group

Involucrati, with diphyllous spathes, ciliated margins to leaves, finely reticulated tunics and scarlet, undivided stigmata.

1.	Stigmata longer than stamens.	2.
	Stigmata shorter than stamens.	3.
2.	Flowers large.	The cultivated Saffron Crocus. var. *Orsinii*.
	Flowers small.	var. *Cartwrightianus*. Greek. var. *Thomasii*. Italian. var. *Haussknechtii*. Very pale. Persian.
3.	No yellow in throat.	4.
	Throat yellow.	6.
4.	Floral segments wide.	var. *Elwesii*.
	Floral segments narrow.	5.

E

5. { Flowers lilac.   *C. olbanus.*
   { Flowers purple.   *C. dispathaceus.*

6. { Flowers generally lilac.   var. *Pallasii.*
   { Flowers generally white.   *C. hadriaticus.*

C. sativus of Linnæus. The cultivated Saffron produces its
grey-green, narrow, ciliated leaves in October before the flowers
appear; these have rounded segments that open out flat in
sunshine, and having once fully opened do not entirely close
again, thus resembling those of the wild Greek form, var.
Cartwrightianus, and a distinct species, also from Greece,
C. Tournefortii, and they are consequently frequently damaged
by rain. In colour they are of a dull reddish lilac, freely veined
with a deeper shade, especially at the throat. Their most noticeable feature is the peculiar pistil, so long that its branches hang
down out of the flower and are a brilliant blood-red. They
widen towards the tips and end in blunt, slightly toothed funnels.

The flowers are so handsome and distinct that they would
be among the best for gardens were it not that the plant is
remarkably shy in producing them except in places with a very
hot summer.

It appears to require frequent lifting and division, and to
appreciate rich but porous soil, and therefore is best suited in
a sunny, sheltered bed where it can be treated as a kitchen
garden crop rather than a border plant. If left alone for more
than three years it will produce nothing but leaves, and the
corms will dwindle to a quarter the size that they ought to
attain if properly divided and manured.

One would like to believe the account of its introduction as
given thus by Hakluyt, 'It is reported at Saffron Walden that a
pilgrim proposing to do good in this country stole a head of
Saffron, and hid the same in his palmer's staffe which he had
made hollow before of purpose, and so he brought the root into
this realme, with venture of his life, for if he had bene taken by
the law of the country from whence it came he had died for the
fact.' There is, however, reason for supposing that it was
introduced to Britain by the Romans.

The variety *Orsinii* is only known from herbarium specimens,
and it is much to be wished that living plants could be found
and introduced to cultivation. George Maw made three

journeys to the neighbourhood of Ascoli in search of it, but was unsuccessful.

The variety *Cartwrightianus* was described as a separate species by Herbert, who named it after Mr. Cartwright, the British Consul at Constantinople. It is plentiful in Greece, and though small in flower, with segments generally about an inch in length, it flowers so freely in English gardens that it is very attractive on sunny slopes of a rock garden in October and November. Some of the white forms, especially if starred with purple lines in the throat, are particularly beautiful, and look better when mingled with the coloured forms than when kept separate. The corm is at times as large as that of a well-grown Saffron Crocus, and about an inch and a half in diameter.

I have collected this plant on the hard-trodden soil of a cavalry exercising ground below Hymettus, where, though abundant, it was a very difficult and painful task to dislodge any with a fern trowel. Later I found it on the lower slopes of Lycabettos under the Aleppo Pines in loose soil, where clumps of its large corms were easily acquired. There also it was plentiful even in the pathways and trodden tracks through the trees, and it seemed a kindness to remove these bruised and suffering individuals for a safer life in gardens.

C. oreocreticus of B. L. Burtt is described and published as a new species in *Phyton*, Vol. I, p. 224 (1949), from specimens collected in Crete.

It is closely related to *C. Cartwrightianus* Herbert, from which it differs in two important characters, having glabrous, unciliated leaves and an unbearded throat. Thus it differs from all other members of the *C. sativus* group. It is also smaller and has shorter, more erect, scarlet stigmatic branches than *C. Cartwrightianus* and is found at much higher altitudes in Crete, which fact is usefully indicated by the epithet *oreocreticus*, from the Greek ορεος, 'belonging to mountains.'

It should be noted that on the same page Burtt advocates the recognition as species of *C. Cartwrightianus* Herbert, *C. Pallasii* Goldbach and *C. Thomasii* Tenore, which although differing so widely in the forms of their flowers have been placed as varieties of *C. sativus*.

The variety *Thomasii* was regarded as a species by Herbert

C. Thomasianus, but Tenore described it earlier as *Thomasii.* It is but little known in cultivation except from a few corms collected by C. C. Lacaita in 1900 at Gravinola, six miles north-west of Taranto in Italy. Some of these were sent to me by the kindness of the Director of Kew, and I have been able to raise a few seedlings from them in some seasons. The corm is smaller than in the Greek variety, the flowers more slender with long and pointed segments, and the stigmata only slightly overtop the anthers. Otherwise they resemble var. *Cartwrightianus* in being of the same peach-blossom tone of rosy lilac, veined with purple especially at the throat, but they vary much less in range of colour.

The variety *Haussknechtii* is a Persian form, and as known in gardens a free-flowering but flimsy-textured variety. It is a great seeder and varies from a dull white to a pale washy lilac, and occasionally with faintly marked stripes. It is one of the poorer forms for garden effect but might give good seedlings if crossed with its handsomer relations.

The variety *Elwesii* is another Eastern form collected by H. J. Elwes and though thin in texture bears large flowers of pleasing shades of lilac obscurely veined with purple. At one time a good white variety was grown at Kew under the name of *C. sativus* var. *cashmirianus,* but I believe it has died out. The flowers of this variety vary in size and the best have segments an inch and a half, or more, in length. The pistil is bright scarlet and shorter than the stamens.

Crocus olbanus of Siehe takes its name from Olba in Cilicia. It has numerous very narrow, almost thread-like, ciliated leaves, greyish-green in colour. In other characters it greatly resembles *C. sativus* var. *Elwesii,* but differs in the shape of its flowers, in which the segments are remarkably long and narrow, about two inches in length and only a quarter of an inch wide in the central and broadest portion. They taper gradually to a pointed apex and are marked, especially on the inner surface, with nine purplish veins on the soft lilac ground colour. The numerous starry flowers are so distinct in appearance that it is a pity the plant has proved difficult to grow in most gardens. The only place I know of where it throve was at Gunnersbury, that happy home of many good plants in the days gone by.

C. dispathaceus is the name which I proposed in 1924 in the first edition of this book for a very distinct plant distributed as *C. tauri* by Georg Egger of Jaffa. Its long and narrow segments, and leaves fine as a hair, are much like those of *C. olbanus*, but many remarkable characters point to specific rank for Egger's plant. The flowers are the deepest vinous purple of any Crocus, a curious shade in which brown madder and red are present. The deep orange pistil is unusually short, its entire stigmatic branches only just appearing in the throat much below the bases of the long, yellow, curving anthers, which are raised on reddish lilac filaments.

Its greatest originality, however, is the possession of a second basal spathe, which is one and three-quarters of an inch in length, lorate and tapering to a fine point which projects above the outer sheathing scales, where it is matched by a second pointed scarious body, which on examination proves to be the tip of the innermost sheathing scale. It is tubular like ordinary sheathing scales to within an inch and a half of its tip, but then becomes open and lorate. I have never seen these characters in any other Crocus.

Unfortunately it was a very shy-flowering plant, and has died out here. It differs from others of the *sativus* group in having a single instead of a double proper spathe, but the ciliated leaves, entire stigmata and finely reticulated silky tunic incline me to connect it with them in spite of its double basal spathe.

The provenance of Egger's plants is unknown. He was a keen hunter as well as plant collector and his excursions took him far afield into remote places. However, in 1950 specimens of this little-known species were received at Kew from Aleppo and he may well have collected it there.

Forms with yellow throats

C. Pallasii was a name used by Goldbach for a form from the Crimea. Maw adopted it to include many forms, with pistils shorter than the anthers, including the Italian var. *Thomasii*. Considering it better to use it only for those that have yellow in the throat I have excepted *Thomasii*. It will then include *C. campestris* of Pallas and Herbert from Bulgaria, *C. Visianicus* of Herbert from Dalmatia, and forms from Corfu, Crete, the Crimea and Turkey in Europe. Those of them that I have grown have small, neatly formed flowers that do not open out quite flat, varying in colour from a rosy lilac to pure white. One very pretty form is rich lilac, with reddish throat and a white margin to the outer segments.

The white forms are very difficult to separate from *C. hadriaticus.*

C. hadriaticus of Herbert was known to him in two varieties.

Var. 1, *chrysobelonicus*, from the hill of Chrysobeloni, in Santa Maura, western Greece. Figures 8 and 9 of his plate 17 in the *Botanical Register* for 1847 show it as a medium-sized flower some two inches in length, white with yellow throat and red-purple lines at the base of the segments outside. As grown here I found that, as Herbert states, it varies in the presence or absence of the red markings.

Var. 2, *Saundersianus*, Herbert described as flowering earlier— in September instead of October and November—and with larger flowers but otherwise similar to the Santa Maura plants. The throat, he says, is deep golden, sometimes unstreaked, sometimes stained with deep livid reddish purple. Figure 7 of the *Botanical Register*, plate 17, shows it as a very handsome flower. Maw's figure represents a flower without yellow in the throat, but deep purple at the base inside and out, a form that I have never seen, and that looks more like a white form of *C. sativus* itself.

A form that generally throws up the flowers before the leaves has been described as *C. peloponnesiacus* by Orphanides in Boissier's *Diagnoses*, but later Boissier placed it as var. β of *C. hadriaticus.* I noticed it doing well in a bed of mixed Crocuses in Cambridge Botanic Garden, but when grown here it varied from year to year as to the length of leaves at flowering time. It has less yellow in the throat than the others, but is certainly a form of *C. hadriaticus.*

Seedlings from the var. *chrysobelonicus* vary with white or pale lilac flowers, or with fine purple lines on the outer segments, and it is impossible without knowing the parentage of the seedlings to divide them from some forms of *C. sativus Pallasii.*

All the varieties of this group make large corms when growing well, but they seem very liable to disease and attacks by subterranean insects, such as wireworms and the larvæ of *Agrotis segetum*, possibly because the soft silky fibres of the tunic are so easily penetrated. An apparently healthy stock will suddenly fail, and when lifted either empty tunics will be found or corms so badly riddled with holes that they seldom recover.

VII

The Vernus Group

WHAT may be called the *Vernus* group consists of four very closely related species, and one (*C. Malyi*) which is best placed with them although distinct in tunic. *CC. vernus, Tomasinianus* and *Heuffelianus* are of such near kin that it is very difficult to find any structural characters which can be relied upon to distinguish them, and in gardens each has produced hybrids with one or other species of the group. They are spring-flowering, having finely reticulated tunics, usually a basal spathe, a proper spathe of one bract only, flowers of many shades of purple or lilac, and rather wide leaves. They increase rapidly in suitable surroundings by the formation of small corms on various portions of the old corm instead of at the summit only as in so many species.

The normal forms of each species can usually be separated by their general appearance, but when intermediates are in question it is impossible to draw a hard and fast line. The following key should help to distinguish most examples, but variation in the characters referred to may occur:

1. { Throat beardless.   2.
   { Throat bearded.   3.

2. { Filaments and throat white.   *C. Heuffelianus.*
   { Filaments and throat yellow.   *C. species.*
   (see p. 77).

3. { Throat yellow internally.   *C. Malyi.*
   { Tunic fibres parallel.
   { Throat white internally.   4.
   { Tunic fibres netted.

4. { Leaves tapering to both ends.
   { Flowers March to April.
   { Segments rounded, generally striped.   *C. vernus.*
   { Leaves linear.
   { Flowers January to March.
   { Segments pointed, unstriped.   *C. Tomasinianus.*

Crocus vernus of Hill has such a wide distribution in central Europe, from the Pyrenees to the Carpathians, that as might be expected it is one of the most variable. Alpine heights of France, Switzerland, Italy and Austria are sheeted with diminutive forms that together with *Soldanella alpina* pierce through the sodden brown turf even before the covering of snow has melted. I have often seen the Crocus flowers pressing upward against a thin layer of almost transparent snow, and a few hours afterwards widely open in the sunshine which melted away their last film of winter covering. On the St. Gothard the myriads of their white flowers imitate the last drifted patches of snow. The slopes of the Little Mont Cenis produce an endless variety of white, lavender and striped forms which resemble Lilliputian counterparts of many of the well-known garden favourites. Unfortunately these small mountain forms do not grow well in lowland gardens, and generally die out after the third year of exile. On the other hand an equally minute form, known as the var. *siculus* of Tineo, from Sicily is not difficult; and a rather larger, pure white one, with notched tips to its segments, collected by W. R. Dykes on Mount Veljun in Croatia, increases rapidly in the ordinary border.

The most beautiful and largest wild forms I grow were sent me by a generous friend who collected them at Vallombrosa, and many fine violet, purple, or striped varieties might be collected in the Neapolitan province and other parts of Italy. *C. vernus* has been a garden favourite for the last three hundred years. It seeds freely and it is hard to find two seedlings exactly alike. Most raisers of seeds are ready to see swan-like superiorities in their own seedlings compared with the mere geese of others, so names beyond numbering have been bestowed on far too many varieties. The group name *C.* × *cultorum* has been given by J. Bergmans to these garden forms of mixed origin.

Some of these garden varieties of *C. vernus*, with the exception of the autumnal *C. speciosus* var. *Aitchisonii*, produce the largest flowers and are the most showy of all Crocuses. They are excellent for bold plantings among deciduous shrubs, either in one variety or mixed, for edgings to borders, and above all for naturalising in grass. Dutch catalogues provide a wide choice, and I will only mention those that are particular favourites of mine.

'Purpureus grandiflorus.' An immense, royal-purple flower, glistening all over with natural polish. Late.

'Madame Mina.' Pale, soft lilac, beautifully striped with a darker shade. Early.

'Kathleen Parlow.' Absolutely pure white. A very long flower.

'Montblanc.' An old, but good, solid white form with a blue throat.

'Margot.' A cool lilac-blue, with pallid exterior. An elegant, well-formed flower ; has disappeared from catalogues.

'Maximilian.' In the same style as 'Margot' but deeper in colour and larger. These two are best planted away from the striped or red-purple varieties, and look as though *C. Tomasinianus* had entered into their pedigree.

Many very robust varieties with very large and numerous flowers have been added to the bulb lists of late years. Among the most effective I would recommend, as a pure white, 'Joan of Arc.' For striped varieties 'Striped Beauty,' which has larger and more substantial flowers than the older favourite 'Sir Walter Scott.'

'Queen of the Blues' and 'Remembrance' are so lovely and free flowering that both should be used for large patches of lilac colour.

'Nigger Boy' is the darkest purple of all, and 'Paulus Potter' is the reddest, almost magenta in colour. 'Vanguard' is remarkable for flowering much earlier than other varieties of *vernus*. It was selected by Mr. Hoog from a variety received from Russia as *C. vernus Petropolowsky*.

Botanical names have been given to several interesting varieties worth including in a collection though less showy than the garden ones.

Var. *albiflorus*—covers the small, white form so common on the St. Gothard.

Var. *siculus*—a minute, star-flowered form (see p. 150) from mountains in Sicily and elsewhere. There is a form in cultivation that has no beard in the throat.

Var. *leucorhyncus*—a large and beautiful form that has become scarce. It is pale lavender with white tips to the segments, the purity of which is enhanced by purple markings shaped like double arches below the white markings, similar to those of *C. Heuffelianus.*

Var. *leucostigma*—a very curious variety in which the rich orange-scarlet of the stigma has disappeared, leaving it a creamy white. It also flowers much earlier than any other form of *C. vernus,* and is peculiarly blue lilac in colour. Its origin is unknown and it cannot be traced beyond a few old gardens.

Var. 'G. Maw' is a quaint freak which has well-formed white flowers, each of the segments of which shows a thickened strip of bright orange running up its centre from the upper-third to the tip, of the same colour and substance as the stigmata. It was sent to George Maw by Miss C. M. Owen, who noticed it and several other monstrous forms in her garden at Knochmullen, Gorey, Ireland. Strange to say, it still retains its peculiarity.

C. Tomasinianus was so named by Dean Herbert after his friend Signor Tommasini* of Trieste. Herbert always spelt the name of both his friend and the plant with a single 'm.' This charming species replaces *C. vernus* on the east of the Adriatic, in parts of Dalmatia, Bosnia and Serbia. As known in present-day gardens it has a short basal spathe and a bearded throat, but Herbert failed to find the basal spathe in those he examined, although he stated that he expected it might be found when a greater number of specimens were available for examination. Maw declared the chief distinction between *C. vernus* and *C. Tomasinianus* lay in the beardless throat of the latter, but I have never seen a specimen without the beard.

C. Tomasinianus has a slender flower bud due to the close wrapping of the segments, reminding one of a smart new umbrella compared with the thicker, clumsier buds of *C. vernus* which are more of the 'gamp' style. In most of its forms the exterior is much paler than the interior, frequently in fact of rather an ashen grey with a dead, 'wrong-side of the fabric' appearance that I have not noticed in any form of *C. vernus* except in 'Margot' and 'Maximilian,' which may have

* This botanist, Muzio de Tommasini (1794-1879), a celebrated investigator of the Dalmatian flora, always wrote his own name with a double 'm' and many authors have consequently amended Herbert's spelling to *Tommasinianus.*

inherited this peculiarity from a cross with *C. Tomasinianus*.
However, with the first rays of sunshine all is changed, for the
outer segments open and expose the clear lavender or amethyst
shades of the inner segments, and when widely open the starry
flowers make a wonderfully fine display.

It is a very early-flowering species, generally opening in
January, and varies widely in shade from pure white to a
glowing amethyst-purple that in some seedlings approaches
nearer to crimson than I have seen in any other Crocus.

I have selected many charming seedlings to grow on into
stocks, and one with white tips and purple marks below them
and slight featherings lower still has appeared at Vincent
Square and received an award of merit. I call it var. *pictus*, as
the white and purple markings look so much as though they
are painted on to a pale flower. It appeared as a chance seedling
in my rock garden, and I do not think it derives the painted tip
from *C. vernus* var. *leucorhyncus*, but is probably a reversion to a
form similar to one mentioned by Herbert as having a dark
blotch.

Other seedlings show the influence of *C. vernus*, some so
strongly that but for their early flowering and characteristic
linear leaves they might be passed over as smaller forms of
C. vernus.

White seedlings have so far proved disappointing, as the
absence of pigment has been associated with narrow segments
of thin substance. Their starry blooms are pretty when scattered
among the mass of lilac brethren but not good enough to be
selected for growing on.

Rosy forms almost the colour of peach blossom are lovely,
and a little potful gained an A.M. some years ago as var. *roseus*.

One with a white tip to its pale lavender segments looks like
a piece of Wedgwood china when examined closely, and bears
the name 'Bobbo' to remind me of the sharp-eyed boy who was
the first to spot it.

A late-flowering seedling I call 'Versitom,' because its creamy
white flowers are faintly veined with lilac on the inner surface
of all the segments, which clearly points to a cross between
versicolor and *Tomasinianus*.

I hope I may someday find a rose-coloured form with a

deep red-purple spot below a white tip, in fact a red variety of *pictus*.

C. Tomasinianus is one of the best for seeding freely and will appear along edges of paths and where rubbish weeded from the borders has been stacked, but is ever welcome except when it invades patches of other and rarer species. It is one of the plants that have received the Wisley Award of Garden Merit as worthy of inclusion in every garden.

C. Heuffelianus of Herbert comes from Hungary and Transylvania, but is insufficiently robust and free of increase to become widely popular. It flowers earlier than *C. vernus*, and as we know it is of a deep reddish-purple, with a very distinct darker marking near the tip of each segment, but only on the outer surface. The inner segments have a little notch in their tips which is very characteristic of this species, and together with its beardless throat helps to distinguish it from somewhat similarly coloured forms of *C. vernus*.

The leaves are less evident at flowering time than in its allies, and the general appearance of the plant reminds me of the autumnal *C. nudiflorus* and *C. asturicus*.

This plant, originally named *C. banaticus* by Johann Heuffel in 1835, was renamed by Herbert as *C. Heuffelianus* because J. Gay had already in 1832 applied the epithet *banaticus* to another species. An intricate web of mixed nomenclature envelops these Eastern species, and awaits someone with more time and patience than I should care to give to its disentanglement.

The confusion was increased by the importation from the Carpathians of a very beautiful late-flowering species under the name of "*C. Heuffelianus*," which needs a new name.

It can be distinguished at a glance from the three foregoing species by the golden-yellow throat and filaments, and the rosy-lilac ground colour of its chubby, rounded flowers.

This close relative of both *C. vernus* and *C. Heuffelianus* approaches the former in its rounded segments and the latter by generally having a beardless throat. I have detected a slight tuft of hair on the inner segments only, of one or two specimens, and there is no basal spathe in some others.

The extraordinary amount of variation shown by these four

allied forms almost certainly indicates that they are derivatives from one original stock and have not yet become thoroughly fixed.

This Carpathian species is therefore of special interest, and the additional character of yellow in the throat suggests great possibilities in future variation. Seedlings I have raised vary greatly. One is very handsomely marked with purple, and flowers earlier than the others, its buds appearing before its remarkably wide leaves. I recommend this beautiful little species to those who will take up the work of raising seedlings.

C. Malyi of Visiani is limited to the Velebit Mountains in Croatia, and has been collected on Monte Vermaz, Monte Orjen, and more recently by Mr. Dykes above Carlopago, near Sinokos.

It is a handsome species with large flowers so slightly tinted with rose colour as to appear almost white, and a rich yellow throat more or less marked externally with brownish-red. It looks as though it were closely related to *C. vernus*, but the yellow throat and filaments, the diphyllous proper spathes and a tunic of parallel fibres, distinguish it. There is no difficulty in cultivating it as it is a sturdy species, flowering in March when others are on the wane. The leaves are very short when it begins to flower, and somehow or other it has the look of an autumnal, rather than of a vernal, species. It is named after an Austrian gardener and plant collector, Franz de Paula Maly (1823-91), and not after the more celebrated Joseph Karl Maly (1797-1860), author of a *Flora von Steiermark* and other works.

VIII

The Imperati Group

CROCUS IMPERATI may be selected as the head of another group of closely related species, the most noticeable feature of which is the contrast in colour between their inner and outer segments.

When in bud or closed for the night, and when the weather is overcast they appear altogether buff or straw-coloured, but directly the flowers open and the inner segments are revealed the somewhat inconspicuous bud becomes a strikingly conspicuous flower. This is due to the bright lilac, rosy mauve, or occasionally pure white of the inner segments.

I should like to think that *C. Cambessedesii* is either the ancestral form from which this group has developed or a close relation thereto. If we trace their geographical distribution on a map of southern Europe it needs but little imagination to arrange something like a family tree for them.

We start in Majorca, in the Balearic Isles, the headquarters of the diminutive *C. Cambessedesii*. This species is so pallid in its internal tinge of lilac and outer wash of buff, delicately feathered with purplish grey, that it looks like a mere sketch of the richer colouring and greater size of the species that rather untruthfully possesses the name of *C. minimus*. We move our pointer about one degree eastward on the map and touch Sardinia, the southernmost home of *C. minimus*, which also extends its range northward into Corsica, where it abounds as the Crocus of the coast and lowlands. In higher ground it is replaced by its larger relative *C. corsicus*, which is not found on the mainland of Italy. *C. etruscus* is the species found in the Tuscan Maremma opposite the northern half of Corsica, and although some of its feathered forms closely resemble *C. corsicus* as to flower the more coarsely netted tunic of *C. etruscus* shows it to be a different species. Farther south in the environs of Rome it is the fragrant, star-shaped species *C. suaveolens* that represents the family. This is an extremely interesting plant when regarded as a link between its neighbouring species, for it inhabits a very limited region and shows scarcely any traces of variation. Yet with a little more colour in the stigmata and markings of the flower it would approach *C. corsicus* and *C. Imperati*, while a stronger mesh of fibre in the corm tunic would make it very difficult to separate from *C. etruscus*.

C. suaveolens does not spread into the district occupied by *C. Imperati*, which stretches from the Bay of Naples southward into northern Calabria. Had it been otherwise it seems inevitable that hybrid intermediates would occur. A well-marked form grown in gardens and whose source I have never been able to trace strongly suggests a hybrid origin. It might, however, be a variant of a form of *C. Imperati* only found in the mountains of Sardinia, the wild type of which has not yet been introduced to cultivation. Further particulars of these two forms will be found under *C. Imperati* var. *monophyllus* and var. *sardoae*.

On the opposite shore of the Adriatic we find *C. dalmaticus*, a near relation of *C. etruscus*, which forms a link between the latter and the more eastern species *C. Sieberi* and *C. veluchensis*.

If we can imagine the existence of an intermediate form, now lost, we may trace another branch of this family tree from the Corsican *C. corsicus* and the Tuscan *C. etruscus*, ending in *C. versicolor* of the Maritime Alps; for, although Maw states the contrary, Herbert in his masterly monograph recorded that there is 'a pale tinge of straw-colour on the sepals,' and I have some forms of *C. versicolor* raised from seed of wild plants collected near Mentone that are externally of as deep a buff as any form of *C. Imperati*.

Herbert wrote : 'There is much affinity between *C. versicolor, Imperatonius, suaveolens* and *insularis*. They extend from Nice to Naples . . . Corsica and Sardinia, and might be united as a group under the name *C. sub-apenninus*.'

It is not easy to arrange a satisfactory key for species so similar in colouring and so variable in markings.

The following may be helpful though not reliable in the case of some varieties:

1. { Inner floral segments plain lilac.   2.
     Inner floral segments white.   7.

2. { Tunic with parallel fibres.   3.
      { Tunic reticulated.   5.

3. { Flowers globular.   4.
      { Flowers starry.   *C. suaveolens.*

4. { Flowers large.   *C. Imperati.*
      { Flowers small.   *C. minimus.*

5. { Tunic fibres coarse.   6.
      { Tunic fibres fine.   *C. corsicus.*

6. { Proper spathe monophyllous.   *C. etruscus.*
      { Proper spathe diphyllous.   *C. dalmaticus.*

7. { Flowers small, inner segments plain.   *C. Cambessedesii.*
      { Flowers large, inner segments feathered. *C. versicolor.*

C. Imperati of Tenore, named in honour of Ferrante Imperato, a sixteenth-century Italian botanist, is a very handsome and easily cultivated species from mountainous districts round Naples, being the largest flowered and most strikingly coloured of this group of Italian species. The open flowers measure three and a half to four inches across, and vary a great deal in their colour and markings. The three outer segments are always tinged with yellow on their outer surface, ranging from a warm buff to pale straw colour, either self-coloured or marked with deep purple lines or feathering. In both cases the contrast of colour of the outer and inner segments is so beautiful that it is impossible to decide whether the more desirable form is the plain or patterned. A partly expanded flower of the unstriped form, sometimes listed as the variety unicolor, seems the perfection of blending in shades of rosy purple and soft yellow, especially when in a strong light both colours can be seen glowing through one another. A coloured plate in *The Garden*, July 19th, 1913, from a drawing by Miss West shows the beauty of this form. On the other hand there is a great charm in the rich crimson-purple markings and infinite variety of pattern of the feathered forms. The best forms have five main stripes, the upper portion of the central one and the outer edges of the others breaking away into shorter veinings like the pinnae of a feather. I have not been successful in growing-on pure stocks of these most striking forms and have come to believe that, unlike other Crocuses, *C. Imperati* has a habit of varying in its markings according to vigour and seasonal changes.

F

Three distinct white forms have been in cultivation, though always scarce. One, a pure white form, was named var. *montanus* by Herbert in the text of the *Botanical Magazine*, t. 3871 (1841), being found on mountains near Naples at 2,000 to 3,000 feet above sea level. It is a true albino, every trace of purple having disappeared. It is therefore snow-white inside, with rich orange throat and stamens and fine scarlet stigmata. The buff of the outer surface has remained and gains in purity and beauty by its white backing. W. Muller of Nucero, near Naples, recorded the find of a few specimens of this form in a chestnut forest and suggested the varietal epithet *nucerensis* for it. It is, however, the same plant as that figured in Maw's monograph, plate 146, fig. 6, under the name of *C. Imperati* var. f. *albiflos*, derived from Herbert's beautiful drawing in the Lindley Library, and *montanus* is the earliest name for this.

Herbert also described as var. *albus* a form sent by Tenore from Naples, in which the outer segments were marked with three stripes, and this form, perhaps the most beautiful of all, grew in George Paul's Broxbourne nursery many years ago. Seedlings from it vary a great deal, but a few in each batch reproduce the fine white and striped form.

There is another form sometimes offered in which the flowers are faintly flushed with lilac, and slightly striped externally. It is a weak grower and not so attractive as the other two.

A distinct variety has been grown in some Dutch nurseries for many years, and hitherto I have failed to trace its origin. It shows little tendency to vary, and only once in many years has it formed seed in this garden. These undesirable characteristics point to the possibility of a hybrid origin and that the whole stock has been derived by increase of corms from a single individual and that it is a clone. It comes into flower early in January, and unlike the wild forms all the buds open within a week of one another instead of in a succession from late December to mid-March. They show the contrasting buff and lilac colouring, but the outer segments do not vary in their markings; there are no more than three purple stripes and the outer two never break away into featherings. The most marked botanical distinctions are found in the proper spathes, which are diphyllous in the Neapolitan forms and regularly monophyllous

in this, and therefore it may be called the variety *monophyllus*.
Its flowers are rather smaller and rounder in outline and paler
in the throat, the perianth tube longer, and the leaves shorter
and more upright at flowering time, than in the typical form.
It is a good border plant, quite hardy and appears punctually
to brighten the dark days of early January.

Martelli described and figured a form from Sardinia as var.
sardoae in which the proper spathe is monophyllous, and it is
possible that this garden plant may have originated from one
collected in Sardinia. He describes it as having a pale lilac
throat, but the curious antler-like branches of the outer
markings, as shown in his figure do not agree with those of the
variety *monophyllus* of gardens.

Variety *Reidii* of Maw, a beautiful rose-coloured variety, was
sent to George Maw by Francis Nevile Reid, and the dried
flower in Maw's herbarium still shows traces of rosy colouring.
It is shown as figs. 4 and 5 on plate XIV of Maw's monograph,
and is described in the text as 'The most remarkable departure
from the type colouring.' In a letter (hitherto unpublished) to
Peter Barr, Mr. Reid wrote as follows: 'It was found on a
hillside some miles from here [Ravello], and although I have
had the district carefully searched . . . only the one bulb was
found. . . . I have often been sorry that I sent it away before I
had obtained seed, but it seemed a pity that Mr. Maw should
not see the flower in its freshness. The figure in his plate gives
no idea of its delicate tints. The petals were rose-pink with a
large white spot at the base of each, interior of sepals rose pink,
with white spot, exterior buff with three brownish feathered
lines. I saw it once at Benthall.'

Unfortunately this precious plant has been lost, and no other
has been found.

Among the few seedlings I obtained from the monophyllous
form one is rose coloured, but though grown in a frame has
not made any offset nor borne any seed.

All the forms of *C. Imperati* rejoice in a well-drained, sunny
situation and so are well fitted for sheltered nooks in a rock
garden, and there the diphyllous forms sow themselves freely.

C. suaveolens of Bertoloni is so distinctly a poor relation of the
rich and important *C. Imperati* that none but those in search of

modest charm and botanical interest need notice it. It is found farther to the north and altogether outside the region occupied by *C. Imperati*. Thus the latter may well be called the Neapolitan and *C. suaveolens* the Roman Crocus, being found in the Campagna, the Val d'Inferno and the Botanic Garden of Rome, and about as far south as Fundi. It is a slender, pallid likeness of *C. Imperati*, and but for its distinct habitat and conservative principles as to variation has little to distinguish it from that much more beautiful plant.

It comes true from seed in cultivation and the stripes on the outer segments show no tendency to become feathered. The starry outline, smaller dimensions, and a slight amount of reticulation of the upper part of its tunic not found in *C. Imperati* are the most reliable distinctions between the two.

C. etruscus of Parlatore is easily recognised among the buff and lilac species by its coarse, netted tunic, which is even more wiry than that of *C. dalmaticus*, and is furnished below with a separate star-shaped, rayed disc, the basal tunic, which is absent in *C. dalmaticus*.

It is a native of the west coast of Italy and is only found in the Tuscan Maremma. It has a large well-formed flower, not so bright in colour as that of *C. Imperati*, and frequently more grey than buff in its outside colouring. It varies greatly in the extent of feathering, the most richly marked forms closely resembling *C. corsicus*, the plainest approaching *C. dalmaticus*.

A more robust, larger variety has been raised in Holland and named 'Zwanenburg variety' after that famous garden.

The ground colour is much bluer than in the type, and it received the A.M., Haarlem, in 1939. Another form with rosy pink colouring has also been selected over there, and when sufficiently plentiful will be a charming companion to the other.

C. minimus of De Candolle is by no means the smallest of the family, being larger in all its parts than its near relative *C. Cambessedesii* and the equally diminutive *C. cyprius* and *C. Pestalozzae*. Wild specimens of *C. minimus* can generally boast of a length of an inch to an inch and a quarter for the outer segments, and some seedlings I have raised have flowers of over an inch and a half, while those of the others mentioned do not exceed three-quarters of an inch in length.

It may be described as an octavo edition, the diphyllous form of *C. Imperati* representing the folio and *C. Cambessedesii* a duodecimo.

The buff ground of the outer segments of *C. minimus* varies in the richness or entire lack of purple featherings as much as in *C. Imperati*, and a pure white form has been found. It is plentiful along the west coast of Corsica and up to an altitude of about 2,000 feet, but is found in higher levels in Sardinia.

C. minimus is a sturdy little plant in cultivation, easily grown on sunny ledges of the rock garden, but does not increase freely except by seed. It flowers over a long period in its island homes from January to April, according to elevation, and most of those that have come my way seem to be from its higher habitats, as they are generally among the last Crocus flowers of the spring, frequently lasting on into the middle of April, with the white variety *lacteus* of *C. aureus*, and the latest garden forms of *C. vernus*.

The richly feathered forms are very beautiful and the rounded ends of the segments give it a charm and distinction which always make it welcome even though its appearance heralds the close of another Crocus season.

C. corsicus of Maw was confused by most of the earlier writers with *C. minimus* and included with it under the name of *C. insularis*. It is the var. I *major* of Herbert, and in his beautiful drawing t. 21 (1843) of Vol. *29*, new ser. *6*, of the *Botanical Register* the two larger flowers at the back of the group are certainly *C. corsicus* and the others represent *C. minimus*.

It is common in the mountains of Corsica, generally at a higher level than that reached by *C. minimus*, and continues up to 7,000 feet above sea-level.

Its greater size, monophyllous spathe, finely reticulated tunic, and paler flowers with conspicuously scarlet stigmata, distinguish it from *C. minimus*.

In the garden it is less effective than its relations and parsimoniously unobliging as to increase, either by offsets or seeds.

C. Cambessedesii was named by J. Gay after Jacques Cambessedes (1799-1863), a French botanist who published a flora of the Balearic Isles in 1827. One of the daintiest of all, this tiny species with leaves like fine grass and flowers less than an inch in length looks as though the Fairy Queen had tried to make a Crocus for a doll's house.

It is found only in Majorca and Minorca in the Balearic Isles, but is plentiful there in woods and heathy ground, flowering throughout the autumn and until the end of March. This habit makes it rather tender for the open ground, and it is best grown in an unheated frame, but although the long succession of flowers makes it interesting it prevents it making much show at any one time.

The flowers are pale lilac or white, the outer segments straw-coloured externally and variously feathered with delicate designs in deep purple. Brilliant scarlet stigmata give a final touch of beauty to a flower that in spite of its diminutive size is to the connoisseur of Crocuses what a miniature is to a life-sized portrait.

C. dalmaticus of Visiani, although found on the eastern shore of the Adriatic and with much in common with a group of species spreading out to the eastward, yet has a certain amount of family resemblance with this group of Italian Crocuses, and forms a link between them and those that may be centred round *C. Sieberi*.

Its strongly fibred, netted tunic and the absence of a basal spathe connect it with *C. Sieberi*, while the absence of any trace of basal tunic reminds us of *CC. Imperati, corsicus* and *minimus*, in which the fibres of the main tunic are similarly continued to the base of the corm.

There are three distinct forms in cultivation: (*a*) with buff exterior, (*b*) of a uniform greyish lavender, and (*c*) flushed throughout with rosy lilac. Maw mentions a white form in the island of Lesina that still awaits the well-timed arrival of some keen-eyed collector. It must not be confused with the pure white form of *C. biflorus* var. *Weldenii*, which is plentiful in Dalmatia and has frequently appeared in lists as *C. dalmaticus* var. *niveus*.

The garden value of *C. dalmaticus* has been overlooked and it is too seldom planted. It flowers early in February and is generous with its blossoms, they open widely on mild days and set seed freely if visited by hive bees.

C. versicolor was described under this name in 1808 by John

Bellenden Ker, whose name was then Gawler. This change of name should be borne in mind when looking up references of that date, for names are followed by the words Ker, Gawl., or Gawler, each of which refers to this author.

The vol. 27 of the *Botanical Magazine* contains his description together with a figure, t. 1110.

It is abundant along the French Riviera from sea-level to an altitude of 4,000 feet in the Maritime Alps, and extends from the hills east of the Rhône to the Italian frontier, and as far northward as Grenoble.

The markings of the flowers are very variable, but, except in a few white-grounded forms, a constant character is found in the feathered markings on the inner segments. This is so unusual in Crocuses that it may be relied upon to distinguish *C. versicolor* from all other spring-flowering species.

Some forms of *C. vernus* have a few lines or featherings on their inner segments, but they are not so conspicuous on the inner surface as in the case of *C. versicolor*.

C..nevadensis has delicately branched lines on the inner surface, but is so distinct in all other characters, especially in the semi-cylindrical leaves, that it could not be confused with these others.

C. versicolor has parallel fibres in its tunic, a basal spathe and monophyllous proper spathe. In wild specimens the flowers are somewhat starry with narrow segments. Garden-raised seedlings show improvement in size; and beautiful forms with rosy suffusion or rich purple markings may be raised in a few generations.

The name *versicolor* is found in Parkinson's *Paradisus* (1629), and his Nos. 7, 8 and 9 most likely represent this species. Miller's Party-coloured Crocus and Broad-leaved Spring Crocus are also forms of *C. versicolor*.

It was at one time a favourite garden plant and eighteen named varieties are included in Sabine's account of Spring Crocuses, published in 1829-30. Very few of these remain in cultivation at the present time. A few lists contain, as the 'Cloth of Silver', an old form that was known under that name, and also as *C. versicolor* 'Morleon' a hundred years ago. It has a white ground, slightly tinted with lilac and striped with purple.

The best form is sold as var. *picturatus*, in which the contrast between the pure white ground and rich purple external stripes is very striking.

The variety *purpureus* is also obtainable, but is rather dull in colouring, having somewhat indefinite veinings on a cloudy lilac ground. The anthers in this variety are generally malformed and at times altogether wanting.

IX

The Eastern Reticulate Species

C. susianus and *C. Sieberi* are the best-known examples of this group. The latter is one of the Crocuses that have received the Award of Garden Merit of the Royal Horticultural Society, a distinction instituted to point out plants that should be included in every garden.

The species may be distinguished as follows:

1. { Flowers lilac or white.   2.
    { Flowers yellow.   5.

2. { Flowers globular.   3.
    { Flowers starry.   *C. reticulatus.*

3. { Throat lilac or white.   *C. veluchensis.*
    { Throat not lilac.   4.

4. { Throat orange.   *C. Sieberi.*
    { Throat yellow or white.   *C. dalmaticus.*

5. { Flowers globular.   6.
    { Flowers starry.   7.

6. { Leafless at flowering time.   *C. gargaricus.*
    { Leaves with flowers.   *C. ancyrensis.*

7. { Flowers banded with brown.   *C. susianus.*
    { Flowers feathered.   *C. stellaris.*

Mr. B. L. Burtt has published in the *Journal R.H.S.*, Vol. LXXIV, Part 1 (January 1949), the result of a very thorough investigation of the status of the many different names used in a specific or varietal sense for *C. Sieberi* of Gay.

In this article it is clearly shown that the beautiful, early-flowering, lilac plant gardeners have regarded as the typical form of *C. Sieberi* must take its place as a variety of the equally beautiful but scarce and less easily grown plant from Crete, hitherto called variety *versicolor*.

This happens because when Gay described the white and purple Cretan Crocus the lilac form of the mainland was unknown to him. It would be quite simple if we could get into the way of speaking of these as the Cretan *Sieberi* and the Greek *Sieberi*; but we must not ignore the facts that some botanists have considered that the lilac plants of Greece include two species—distinguished chiefly by distinct areas of distribution and the presence or absence of small tufts of hairs, so-called beards, in the perianth throat.

In 1928 a German botanist, K. Schulz-Korth, proposed the recognition of three species, namely *C. Sieberi* of Gay for the Cretan white and purple form with a glabrous throat, *C. nivalis* of Bory and Chaubard, the lilac form of the Peloponnesus with bearded throat, and *C. atticus* of Orphanides with a more northern distribution, broader leaves, longer anthers and beardless throat.

After careful examination of many living and dried specimens Mr. Burtt has found the southern form is mostly beardless, while among the specimens from Attica both bearded and glabrous forms can be found.

So he considers that as regards *C. Sieberi* the bearded and glabrous throat is not sufficiently uniform in the *nivalis* and *atticus* specimens to prove of taxonomic value, and we need not regard these forms as species.

However, as the name *C. Sieberi* must be attached to the Cretan form of many colours, we need a varietal name to use along with it for the fine lilac Crocus that is so widely grown in gardens.

It is the form from Attica, and so *C. Sieberi* var. *atticus* should be written on our labels, but very probably we shall still speak of it as just "*Crocus Sieberi*."

The self-coloured var. *atticus* is widely distributed in the mountains of Greece. As a garden plant it is one of the easiest species to grow as well as one of the earliest to flower, and should be included in every collection. The flowers vary in depth of lilac from the colour of an amethyst to a shade as pale as that of the old double lilac primrose. The rich orange of the throat and the scarlet stigmata give warmth and brilliancy to the general effect when open in the sunshine, though when closed the general tone is a rather cold, bluish lilac. It has very wide leaves, with blades of a particularly rich but dark green that help to show up the broad, white, central stripe more distinctly than in any of its close relations, providing one of those blessed signatures Nature offers to observant gardeners who desire to keep their stocks true.

The Cretan form, the true *C. Sieberi* of Gay, was introduced to cultivation by the British Consul at Canea who sent roots from the White Mountains in Crete to that prince of collectors and distributors Henry J. Elwes, and afterwards to George Maw. It was then called *C. Sieberi* var. *versicolor* and later var. *heterochromus* in Halácsy's *Conspectus*. Though collectors have recently obtained good supplies it is still scarce in gardens, being a very shy seeder, and somewhat tender.

It begins to flower in gardens only when the lilac form from the mainland is nearly over. It has a very characteristic and distinct way of pushing through the soil, the flower bud wrapped in its two papery spathes appearing simultaneously with the tips of the leaves. It also differs in the great size of its pistil, which is a good deal higher than the anthers, and divides into three widely opened funnels of an intensely brilliant orange-scarlet, very beautiful against the white segments and rich orange throat. The bands or stripes on the outside are of a crimson shade of purple or maroon unknown in any other Crocus.

Mr. Hubert Edelsten succeeded in raising two very beautiful intermediates between the banded Cretan type and var. *atticus*. They have a ground colour of soft rosy lilac, and the outer segments are externally tipped and centrally marked with crimson-purple, the two dark areas being divided by a ring of white which extends to the edge in the lower half of each segment—as shown in figure I of Plate *11*.

This form received a First Class Certificate of the Royal Horticultural Society in 1924 as *Crocus Sieberi* var. 'Hubert Edelsten.' The later seedling 'Lingwood Beauty' is larger and more richly banded with purple. They flower freely and almost as early as the lilac form which was the pollen parent.

In 1923 I found two pure white youngsters among my seedlings, after thirty years of hopeful expectation. The better of these has increased freely and is the best white and orange spring Crocus I know. It is now known as 'Bowles's White,' has received an A.M., and is 'A' in the plate 7 illustrating Mr. Burtt's article in the *Journal R.H.S.* for January 1949.

The wonderfully fine contrast between its pure white perianth with the orange throat and scarlet stigmata is only equalled among Crocuses by the autumnal *C. niveus*.

The late H. J. Elwes gave me a beautiful form which he had from Mount Chelmos in which the upper lilac portion of the flower is sharply divided from the golden throat by a band of pure white, the result being a conspicuously three-coloured flower. Seedlings have varied in the depths of the lilac, but all retain the white band and yellow throat. It flowers after the main display of the lilac var. *atticus* and before the Cretan type, but, as in the latter, the leaves are but little developed at flowering time.

Mr. Burtt and I agreed that this beautiful variety should be called forma *tricolor* to call attention to the three distinct bands of colour. A lady said it looked like a lilac egg in a silver and gold egg-cup—a very apt description.

Mr. Frank Sowels collected it on Mount Chelmos, and Major Pam and I found a pure colony of it in the chestnut forest above Tripolis and a few intermediate forms among the hundreds of freshly awakened buds of var. *atticus* between patches of melting snow on Parnes late in March.

C. veluchensis of Herbert can be distinguished at a glance from *C. Sieberi* by the absence of yellow in its throat and the more slender build of the flowers, the segments though longer being so much narrower. It also has a remarkably small corm, less than half as large as a well-grown one of *C. Sieberi*.

It is stated to be plentiful in the mountains of Greece and Turkey, and to occur in the Balkans, but has been so frequently confused with other species that we must be cautious in accepting the reputed stations. Maw is correct in declaring that the plate in the *Botanical Magazine*, t. 6197 (1875), represents *C. banaticus*, i.e. *C. Heuffelianus*, for he knew that the plants distributed by Max Leichtlin came from the Berlin Botanic Garden, where *C. banaticus* was grown under the name of *veluchensis*.

I first obtained it in 1905 from Mr. G. Reuthe, who received it from an Albanian collector. I flowered it here the following year, and found that it had a weak constitution, like most Crocuses that form small corms. Fresh stocks have been collected recently in Greece and Bulgaria. I find that in these the throat is white in freshly opened flowers and becomes tinged with lilac when they wither, and is distinctly lilac in dried specimens. As Maw only knew *C. veluchensis* by herbarium specimens he described the throat as purple. The Bulgarian forms seem more robust than those I had from Albania and a white form has been collected.

Sometime prior to 1912 the O'Mahony of Kerry collected a Crocus on Mount Rila, in Bulgaria, that agrees in its structural characters with *C. veluchensis*, although in appearance it approaches *C. vernus*, especially in the polished surface and deep purple of its flowers. Somewhat similar forms have come to me under names to which they have certainly no right and it is likely that many beautiful forms may yet come from eastern Europe.

C. reticulatus of Steven ranges from the Adriatic near Trieste to the Caucasus and is consequently a variable plant.

It is unfortunately rather a weakling in cultivation and seldom holds its own in the open ground. It varies from lilac to white, and the outer segments are variously marked with stripes, featherings, or broad bands of purple. The starry shape of its small flowers together with its coarse, netted tunic afford the readiest means of recognising it.

At one time corms of *C. reticulatus* were collected and sold under the name of "*C. tauri*."

In the variety *micranthus* the flowers are less than an inch in length and the anthers are generally dark grey instead of yellow.

A white form from Romania is a dainty little thing, but very delicate even when allowed the luxury of a cold frame.

C. gargaricus of Herbert is small and dwarf, but so brilliant in its rich orange colouring that it is one of the best of early-flowering species. It has been collected in the Troad on Mount Gargarus, and on the Bithynian Olympus (Ulu-dag) above Bursa (Brusa).

The corms are very small and round and when of flowering age are about the size of a large pea. Many offsets are formed when the plant is happy, some of which are so small that they are hard to find. Even the smallest can be recognised by their finely netted coats, which are yellower than those of other species. The parent bulb throws out long, white runners which push away to the side or downwards for several inches and finally form small pilules or cormlets at their growing tips. By these means the offsets are formed away from the older corms and often get mixed among neighbouring plants. This increase by means of underground stolons is also found in *C. nudiflorus* and *C. lazicus* but in no other species.

As it is such an inveterate wanderer I have never succeeded in inducing it to settle down in a happy family gathering and so provide a little patch of its glowing orange flowers. By copying the methods of a very clever gardening friend I am trying a concentration camp treatment and collecting any stray specimens to be planted in a pan sunk in the ground, where, like Sterne's starling, they 'can't get out.'

C. susianus of Ker, the Cloth of Gold Crocus, is an old inhabitant of Dutch and English gardens, having been sent to Clusius from Constantinople in 1587.

In the *Rariorum Plantarum Historia* Clusius gives a vivid account of the withered condition of the roots when he received them in October, although they had been dug up in spring, as was shown by the dried leaves and flowers still attached to them. It is pleasant to read his account of their progress and to learn that though leaves only were produced in the following spring his care was rewarded by flowers in 1590.

I have frequently had a like experience with collected Crocuses. If dug up in full flower the new corms will generally be sufficiently developed to ripen well enough to grow but not to flower in the following season. Sufficient nutriment usually remains in the old corm to build up a new one, but it is likely to be very small. It is safer to pack them for a long voyage as dry as possible, for if shut in an airtight tin while at all damp they will almost certainly rot.

In 1629 Parkinson described in his *Paradisus* the two varieties of the Cloth of Gold Crocus that are still grown, one with 'three faire and great stripes of a faire deep purple colour' on the back of 'every of the three outer leaves,' the other differing only in having these outer segments 'wholly of the same deepe purple colour on the back of them, saving that the edges of them are yellow, which is the forme of a Duke Tulipa, and from thence it took the name of Duke Crocus.'

There is a beautiful figure of *C. susianus* in the *Botanical Magazine*, t. 652, that clearly shows one of its chief characteristics, the habit of reflexing under the influence of sunshine or the warmth of a room.

The epithet *susianus* is misleading, as Susa, close down by the Persian Gulf, is beyond the limits of any Crocus, and the species in question has a rather restricted range in south-west Russia and the Crimea. An alternative name is *C. angustifolius*.

It is easily grown, and the starry, deep yellow flowers open widely on the sunny days of early February.

C. stellaris of Haworth, figured in *Trans. Hort. Soc. London 1*, t. 6 (1809), is a mysterious plant known only in gardens, and nothing at all like it has been found growing wild. It looks as though it might be a hybrid between *C. susianus* and some form of *C. aureus*, and Maw's objection that there is no authentic record of a hybrid Crocus no longer holds good, as *C. Tomasinianus* with *C. vernus*, and *C. speciosus* with *C. pulchellus*, often produce intermediates.

I should like to believe that it is Parkinson's No. 26, *Crocus vernus versicolor pallideluteus*, though I should be loth to use such a name for it. He writes 'we have a third sort of this kinde of cloth of gold crocus, which hath leaves and flowers like the former, but differeth in this, that the colour of the flower is of a paler yellow by much, but stript in the same manner as the first, but with a fainter purple colour: the roote also is netted like them.'

It has become rather scarce of late, and I find it less vigorous than it was twenty years ago, and possibly it is on the way to dying out.

When doing well it is a pleasing flower owing to the five well-feathered stripes on the outer segments.

It is quite sterile and the anthers and pistil are evidently imperfect, being very small and pallid.

C. ancyrensis of Maw, the Ankara Crocus, was known to

Dean Herbert, who grew and flowered it at Spofforth, but looked upon it as a variety of *C. reticulatus*.

He was, however, decidedly a 'lumper' where Crocuses were concerned, as may be seen by his regarding *C. susianus* and *C. dalmaticus* also as mere varieties of *C. reticulatus*. Maw was the first to describe *C. ancyrensis* as a species. He rightly relied on its blunt, rounded segments to distinguish it from *C. susianus*, in which they are always narrower and taper to a point, but his description of them as 'invariably self-coloured' is no longer true. In 1901 I noticed one plant among many of the typical plain yellow, in which the outer segments were feathered with dull brown markings. It was marked and seeds saved from it produced a strain of variously feathered and suffused forms. In one form which I call var. *suffusus* the general tint of orange is deepened by this suffusion.

C. ancyrensis is plentiful in central Asia Minor near Ankara, Sivas, Kayseri and Maras. It is hardy and easily grown and one of the earliest of yellow species to flower, generally appearing here in January soon after the first blooms of *C. chrysanthus* have opened. In shape, size and colour it is so much like the wild type form of *C. chrysanthus* that it is not always easy to distinguish by the flowers only. Fortunately typical *C. chrysanthus* almost always has minute black spots on the barbs of its anthers which are not found on those of *C. ancyrensis*. The netted tunic of the latter and the smooth coriaceous tunic with basal rings of *C. chrysanthus* distinguish them infallibly if they can be dug up for examination.

C. ancyrensis is illustrated in the *Botanical Magazine*, vol. 167 t., n.s. 99 (1950).

1   CROCUS VALLICOLA

'I always found it a delicate plant . . . but C Wolley-Dod used to succeed well with it in his stiff clay soil near Malpas, Cheshire.'

2   CROCUS SPECIOSUS
'Left to go its own way it will spread freely in borders and even under
deciduous shrubs, and then provides carpets and mimic pools of blue
in September as rich as those of bluebells in May.'

3   CROCUS PULCHELLUS
'As the white form is of good substance, it is one of the most beautiful
of early autumnal albino forms.'

4   CROCUS SATIVUS
'. . . the crocus of the ancient world, having been cultivated and prized
from a remote period for the sake of its scented stigmata, which after
careful drying provide the drug Saffron.'

5 CROCUS TOMASINIANUS
'. . . with the first rays of sunshine . . . the outer segments open and
expose the clear lavender or amethyst shades of the inner segments,
and when widely open the starry flowers make a wonderfully fine
display.'

6   CROCUS ETRUSCUS
'It is a native of the west coast of Italy and is only found in the Tuscan
Maremma . . . it varies greatly in the extent of feathering.'

7   C R O C U S   C O R S I C U S

'It is common in the mountains of Corsica, generally at a higher level than that reached by Crocus minimus, and continues up to 7,000 feet above sea-level.'

8   CROCUS KOROLKOWII
'... might be called the Celandine Crocus, for its flowers are starry in shape when widely expanded, and the inner surface shines as though newly varnished ...'

9   CROCUS GRAVEOLENS

'would . . . be recognisable anywhere . . . by the abominable odour
that is perceptible, even at a distance of some yards, when its small
flowers are open on a sunny day.'

10   CROCUS CHRYSANTHUS

'It is the most variable species known as regards colour, the ground colour being sulphur yellow, orange, white or lilac, while the outer segments show every imaginable degree of freckling, suffusion and feathering . . .'

11 CROCUS CHRYSANTHUS 'E. A. BOWLES'
'I admired it so much when I first saw the blossoms Mr Hoog sent me
from Haarlem that he kindly sent me corms and named it after me. I
am very proud of my namesake.'

COLCHICUM SPECIOSUM ALBUM
'The snow-white goblets of good form, equal to that of a Tulip
standing on soft emerald-green tubes, cannot be equalled for beauty
in the late autumn by any other plant so easy to grow well in the
open.'

13   COLCHICUM AGRIPPINUM

'The flowers of Colchicum agrippinum appear early, frequently in the
end of August . . . in some parts of Suffolk and Surrey (it) has become
established in orchards and pastures . . .'

14   COLCHICUM 'WATERLILY'
'Mr J J Kerbert . . . used the pollen of the double-flowered Colchicum
autumnale album on Colchicum speciosum album, from which cross
the enormous pink, double-flowered variety 'Waterlily' was obtained.'

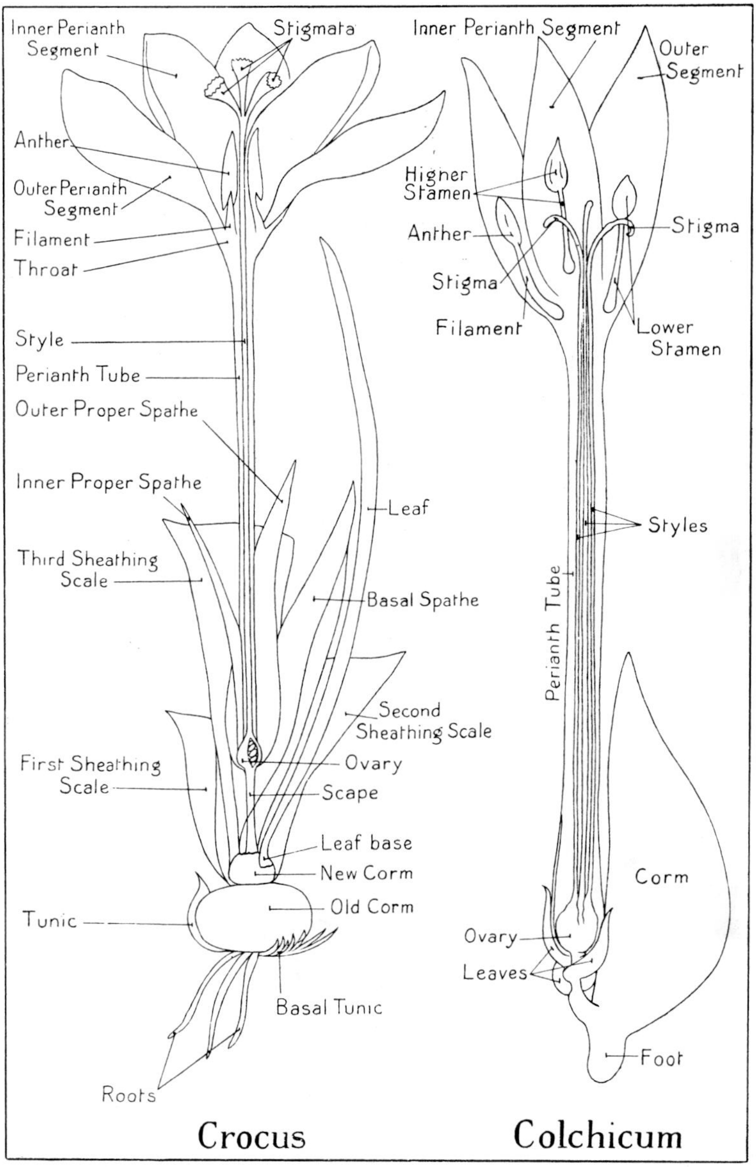
Inner Perianth Segment
Stigmata
Anther
Outer Perianth Segment
Filament
Throat
Style
Perianth Tube
Outer Proper Spathe
Inner Proper Spathe
Leaf
Third Sheathing Scale
Basal Spathe
Second Sheathing Scale
First Sheathing Scale
Ovary
Scape
Leaf base
New Corm
Old Corm
Tunic
Basal Tunic
Roots
Crocus
Inner Perianth Segment
Outer Segment
Higher Stamen
Anther
Stigma
Stigma
Filament
Lower Stamen
Styles
Perianth Tube
Corm
Ovary
Leaves
Foot
Colchicum

15 The parts of Crocus and Colchicum

16   CROCUS KOTSCHYANUS LEUCOPHARYNX

'... a very pretty Crocus that has been listed and grown in gardens for
the last forty years as Crocus karduchorum, because under that name
it was introduced by W Siehe of Mersina who collected it in Cilicia.'

CROCUS LONGIFLORUS
⅕ natural size
'It flowers in October and into November and is very hardy and
reliable in the open border.'

18   CROCUS SATIVUS

'The flowers are so handsome and distinct that they would be among
the best for gardens were it not that the plant is remarkably shy in
producing them, except in places with a very hot summer.'

19   CROCUS TOMASINIANUS
CROCUS TOMASINIANUS PICTUS
'the white and purple markings look so much as though they are
painted on to a pale flower.'

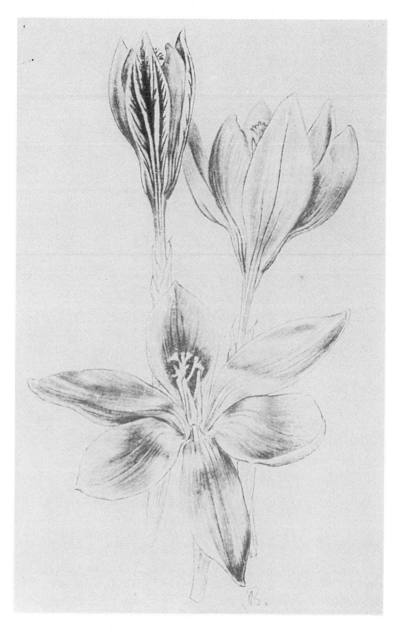

20 CROCUS IMPERATI, FEATHERED AND PLAIN FORMS
'The open flowers measure three and a half to four inches across, and
vary a great deal in their colour and markings.'

21   i Crocus corsicus   ii Crocus suaveolens
            iii Crocus minimus   iv Crocus etruscus

22   CROCUS DALMATICUS

'It flowers in early February and is generous with its blossoms, they
open widely on mild days and set seed freely if visited by hive bees.'

23   CROCUS SIEBERI VARIETIES
i Hubert Edelsten   ii atticus
iii tricolor   iv Sieberi

24   CROCUS VELUCHENSIS
¾ natural size
'. . . has a remarkably small corm, less than half as large as a
well-grown one of Crocus Sieberi.'

25   CROCUS KOROLKOWII

'The small flowers are stained externally with a faint brown speckling merging into dull green at the throat.'

26   CROCUS CANDIDUS SUBFLAVUS

¾ natural size

'The wide leaves and freely produced flowers make it a very attractive
and distinct plant for borders and the rock garden.'

27   CROCUS CHRYSANTHUS VARIETIES
i White Egret   ii Snow Bunting   iii John Hoog
iv Zwanenburg Bronze   v Golden Pheasant

28   CROCUS CHRYSANTHUS 'BULLFINCH'

'. . . a remarkably round flower, creamy yellow, richly feathered with crimson-purple outside, pure white within but for its orange throat.'

29   CROCUS HARTMANNIANUS
¾ natural size
'It is found on the southern slopes of Kiornia in open places in the
forests above the monastery of Makhaeras about 880 metres above
sea level and flowers in mid-February.'

30   CROCUS FLEISCHERI
¾ natural size
'The finely divided stigmata are . . . of such a bright colour that they
can be seen through the white segments of a closed flower, and
remind me of the yolk seen through the shell of a woodpecker's egg.'

31 COLCHICUM ALPINUM
'First of the genus to flower, often appearing in the first days of
August, its flowers ... about an inch in length.'

32   COLCHICUM BOWLESIANUM

'... varies a good deal in the intensity of the dark squares ... and (is)
not evenly chequered all over.'

The Aureus Group

THE majority of yellow-flowered species belong to a group without a basal spathe, and with membranous tunics, which, towards the base, split up more or less into parallel fibres. They inhabit eastern Europe and Asia Minor, with the exception of *C. Korolkowii*, which is found in central Asia, in Bukhara, and as far as the northern frontier of Afghanistan.

They flower in spring, with leaves well developed, but *C. vitellinus* from Syria, which frequently precedes the others and is in flower before Christmas, may be regarded as the last of the autumnal species if we are ready to dissociate it from the evil-smelling *C. graveolens*, generally regarded as a later-flowering variety of it.

Other yellow-flowered species are dealt with among those with reticulated tunics, and there remain only the autumnal, naked-flowering *C. Scharojanii*, from the Caucasus, *C. lazicus*, which has not yet been introduced from Trebizond, and *C. chrysanthus*, which belongs to a distinct group in which the tunics are split into rings at the base.

This *aureus* group is aggravatingly puzzling to botanists and has been much confused in the past, for some of the earlier describers were insufficiently acquainted with the allied species to be able to point out the differences between them. Only a careful study of the wild plants as they grow in their homes can decide some of the points in question. For garden purposes it seems best to divide them into eight species, which can be distinguished thus:

1. { The three stigmatic branches undivided. 2.
{ The stigmatic branches divided. 3.

2. { Leaves few (about five), upright. *C. aureus*.
{ Leaves many (12 or more), spreading. *C. Korolkowii*.

3.	Stigmatic branches divided into six threads.	4.
	Stigmatic branches divided into more than six threads.	5.
4.	Leaves narrow.	*C. Suterianus.*
	Leaves wide.	*C. Olivieri.*
5.	Leaves narrow.	6.
	Leaves wide.	7.
6.	Flowers sweetly scented.	*C. vitellinus.*
	Flowers with unpleasant scent.	*C. graveolens.*
7.	Tunic split into strands in lower half only.	*C. Balansae.*
	Tunic split into strong strands throughout.	*C. candidus.*

Crocus aureus of Sibthorp and Smith is the name selected by botanists from its many aliases for the wild plant that, at some distant period and in some unrecorded place, founded a clan of widely differing garden plants. Nearly all of these are now sterile, and although the wild plant seeds freely no new nor any repetitions of the old forms appear among the seedlings. This is no great evil, as the rich orange colour and early appearance of its flowers proclaim the typical form the best of its race.

It is the most western of all yellow species, ranging from western Asia Minor and the Dobrudja on the east, as far west as Serbia.

It is an old inhabitant of English gardens, and the plant that Gerard received from Jean Robin of Paris, which he described as having 'flowers of a most shining yellow colour, seeming afar off to be a hot glowing cole of fire.' This is a good description of the deeper-coloured and best form, most likely the same that Parkinson in 1629 described as 'of a deeper gold yellow . . . so that they appear reddish withall.'

This was the only yellow Crocus known to Gerard before 1597, who stated that it was grown in our London gardens and that some of these wild Saffrons had been sent by Clusius. So although it reached Gerard from Robin of Paris it may yet have been the direct offspring of those Clusius received from Belgrade in 1579. It is often listed by nurserymen as *C. moesiacus,* a name given it by Ker in 1805; Maesia, or Mysia Superior, being the classical name for Serbia. It was known in old gardens as *C. lagenaeflorus*, the Gourd-shaped, the name given it in Salisbury's *Paradisus Londinensis*, t. 106 (1808), where there is an excellent figure and description. Another good figure occurs in the *Botanical Magazine*, t. 2986.

This rich orange form is worth acquiring for the garden under any name, and is the best yellow Crocus for planting in shrubberies, where it may seed and spread freely under deciduous trees and shrubs; for though it grows well in full exposure to sunshine it does not object to shade after its leaves are mature. It begins to flower in January and continues till mid-March and is a fine sight on a sunny day. The corm tunic is a reddish brown membrane that splits, especially with age, into strong parallel fibres. The old sheathing leaves, whose bases form the corm tunic, turn a dark brown and remain intact longer than in other species, forming a cap, two or more inches in length, according to the depth of planting. The cap persists for many years where the plant has not been disturbed, and is of great use in keeping an open passage, even in stiff clay, for the young shoot to push through to the surface. It also provided a valuable clue for the recognition and digging out of the right plant when I first collected it in Greece after the flowers had disappeared.

It is strange that Halácsy omitted *C. aureus* from the *Conspectus Florae Graecae* as he must have known the fine figure of it in Sibthorp and Smith's *Flora Graeca*, Vol. I, t. 35, but did not compare it with the orange Crocus that is so plentiful even by the roadside near Tatoi, close to Athens. Apparently Halácsy and the local botanists regarded it as *C. Olivieri*, perhaps because Smith in the *Prodromus* and *Flora Graeca* described the tunic as membranaceous, without veins (enervibus) and shiny, which suggests that of *C. Olivieri*.

However, Smith added 'at last much split and fibrillous,' and in contrasting *C. aureus* with *C. vernus* and *C. flavus* as common in gardens, stated it differed from those in its 'membranous, thin never veined tunic.' Whereas Bauer's beautiful drawing for t. 35 plainly shows parallel fibres in the tunic and the sheathing leaves.

Maw's description is correct and runs thus, 'membranous with narrow fibroid divisions splitting up from the base.'

Again it may be because Sibthorp's specimen was gathered in Thrace, near Sestius, at the narrowest part of the Hellespont, outside the area dealt with by Halácsy.

Anyhow it is far more widely spread in Attica than the very local *C. Olivieri*, for which it had been mistaken, and even Maw stated that it was uncertain whether it occurred in Greece.

When I revisited Greece in 1926 Mr. Shirley C. Atchley, author of *The Wild Flowers of Attica*, very kindly helped our little party of flower seekers by joining our expeditions and guiding us to the localities where he had found the rarer plants.

I wanted to see *C. Olivieri* growing wild, and he led me to a spinney near Tatoi and said, 'Now you are standing on its leaves.' I looked for the very wide leaves spreading on the ground that I expected, but saw only very narrow upright ones, very many to each shoot instead of the two or three at most— so characteristic of *C. Olivieri*. Closer examination revealed the unmistakable cap of red-brown sheathing leaves of the previous season reaching to the ground level, but I could hardly believe my eyes that I had the luck to find *C. aureus* in Greece.

As it grew there among the scrub of oak and *Poterium spinosum* the flowers were over, but on higher ground we found a natural amphitheatre encircled by high rocks draped with Aubrieta, where the grassy floor was starred with the flowers of a very dark blue form of *Anemone blanda*, and among them fresh young flowers of *C. aureus* making as lovely a living picture as I have ever seen.

In 1938 I was again at Tatoi and saw the orange Crocuses in full flower, and was greatly interested in noticing how much they vary. Some were clouded with brown markings on the back of the outer segments, amounting, in a few, to conspicuous brown central stripes. Others were paler on the outside, resembling the colour of the Dutch Yellow, and most of these had three bluish-grey lines at the base like those in the Dutch variety, which points to the likelihood that the favourite old garden plant was derived from the Greek strain rather than the Mysian, in which seedlings seldom show any variation. Both races seed freely in the garden and live up to Gerard's description in resembling 'a hot glowing cole of fire.'

On a dry day in February I generally set fire to the dead tops of a tangle of reed, sedge and coarse grasses in a marshy corner of a rough meadow. On adjoining drier ground *C. aureus* is seeding itself and spreading very pleasantly in the shorter turf. After the main blaze has burnt out the fire will travel along among dry tufts of shorter grasses, mostly as little jets of flame of the size and shape of that of a lighted candle. These burn for a few seconds only and in size and colour they resemble the Crocuses so closely that I feel certain that Sophocles meant *Crocus aureus* when he immortalised its fiery colour so aptly in a line of *Oedipus Colonos*. It occurs in a chorus composed of natives of the district of Colonos, which was the home of Sophocles and where he would have seen the orange Crocuses thrusting through the ground in spring. So as blind old Oedipus groped his way home 'the Crocus broke out like fire at his feet.'

Tennyson must have had this line of Sophocles in mind when writing *Œnone*. In this poem he describes the arrival of the three goddesses for the judgment of Paris, and wrote that they trod upon "the smooth-swarded bower, and at their feet the Crocus brake like fire."

The white form, the variety *lacteus*, is not very robust and consequently scarce, but is a singularly beautiful and refined flower. The white has a gleam of yellow in it, yet is clear and in no wise muddy. It always reminds me of the charm of that flaxen-white hair that compensates so richly in age for the trials of possessing red hair in youth. It flowers last of all the forms of *C. aureus*, and together with *C. minimus* and some varieties of *C. vernus* generally provides the last Crocus flowers of each spring.

There was once a form known as *lacteus penicillatus*, of the same delicate ivory-white, but striped with a very peculiar greenish blue which is well figured in t. 2655 (1826) of the *Botanical Magazine*. I have never seen it and fear that it has died out.

Another rare beauty which forms t. 3869 (1841) of the same work is the variety *lutescens*, and can best be described as apricots and cream, the throat representing the apricots and the colour shading off upwards until it is no deeper than cream at the tips of the segments.

Dean Herbert wrote that four or five were found at Barton Park, in Suffolk, close to the place where *C. aureus* and some other species, doubtless remnants of an old garden, had succeeded in establishing themselves. At one time it had apparently disappeared from cultivation, but like many another rare plant was safely stored in Canon Ellacombe's wonderful garden at Bitton, near Bath. Here, at Enfield, it seems to be short-lived, but hitherto has reappeared occasionally from seed. I believe crossing the variety *lacteus* with typical *C. aureus* might produce similar seedlings.

The Yellow Dutch Crocus, also known as *C. luteus*, is the most widely grown of all forms and if a census of spring-flowering plants could be taken would probably head the list as prime favourite. Although its flowers are not so richly coloured nor so early as those of the wild type, it certainly deserves to be planted everywhere, from the window-box of a town house to the horticulturally trained landscapes of parklands measured by square miles. Except when attacked by mice or sparrows it seems to be indestructible, comes up all the stronger for being accidentally dug in to a great depth, and continues to flower even when its rapid increase has caused the corms to become a crowded mass of many superincumbent layers. In most gardens it provides the first blaze of colour on the brown soil of the bare borders, and offers the bees their first feast of pollen and honey.

It seems impossible to trace its exact origin. The name, Dutch Yellow, may be no safer guide than those of English Iris and *Scilla peruviana*. The five flowers from one set of sheathing leaves as shown in Parkinson's figure 1, p. 169 of the *Paradisus* (1629), suggest this form, but in the text he states 'the seede hereof is of a brighter colour than in any of the others.' This applies well to the freely produced, crimson seeds of the wild *C. aureus*, but the Dutch Yellow as we now know it is sterile.

John Rea's mention in his *Flora, Pomona, Ceres* 105 (1665), of 'the greatest yellow crocus' with flowers of a deep yellow colour, but as large as the greatest purple, for which it is esteemed' seems to be the first unquestionable reference to it. Rea says further that this *Crocus luteus maximus* was raised from the seed of the *Crocus luteus sive moesiacus*, which is the true Crocus of Mesia, then 'so common and well known that it needed no description.' He describes the flowers as 'in some of a deep yellow colour, like a cole of fire, in others more pale, and there is one whose flowers are of a Brimstone colour,' which certainly denotes forms of the wild *C. aureus.*

I have dealt lengthily with this common plant because it is one of the most extraordinary in cultivation. It is certainly of garden origin, nothing quite like it having been found wild. It appeared at least two hundred years ago, and possibly in more than one place and form, because there are at least three distinct stocks of it in cultivation, varying in the colour of the outer segments, both in a lighter and duller shade of yellow in some, and also in the length and depth of colour of the grey stripes invariably present, but most marked in the richer-coloured forms.

It is often stated that plants lose in vigour if propagated only by vegetative processes, such as cuttings or divisions. However, the Dutch Yellow and *C. sativus* retain undiminished vigour though they never produce seed. Parallel cases may be found in the old Double Daffodil, the Double Snowdrop and the Jerusalem Artichoke, all of which have been widely cultivated for centuries by division.

C. aureus var. *sulphureus* comprises another and weaker race of seedlings which must have been raised in gardens from *C. aureus,* possibly earlier than the large Dutch Yellow.

They are depauperate forms, forming smaller corms with narrower leaves and slender, pale-coloured flowers. The best account of these is found in a paper by Joseph Sabine read in 1829 and published in Vol. 7, 419-98 (1829-30), of the *Transactions of the Horticultural Society,* of which he was then the secretary. He enumerates five varieties, one of which, *isabellinus,* I have not seen. He rightly recognises Parkinson's *C. vernus flavus striatus* as the *C. sulphureus striatus* so well figured in the *Botanical Magazine,* t. 938 (1806). It has the best constitution of this race and is worth including in a collection, its straw-coloured flowers coming late in the season. His second variety, *striatellus,* is less distinctly striped with purplish brown, and he admits has little merit, being a weak grower. I have only seen this in Miss Willmott's garden at Warley, and Sabine's verdict is too true, for those she gave me have not flourished here.

C. sulphureus concolor, figured in the *Botanical Magazine,* t. 1384 (1811), is still in cultivation and is of a pretty pale yellow without any markings, but not showy enough to be much sought after.

The form known as the variety *sulphureus albidus,* or *pallidus,* is more curious than beautiful, the segments appear bleached at their tips and are also narrowed and somewhat malformed.

The most interesting feature of all four is the atrophied condition of the anthers, which are reduced to minute white arrow-heads and bear no pollen, whereas in all other forms of *C. aureus* the anthers are larger than in other Crocuses of their size.

C. Korolkowii of Regel might be called the Celandine Crocus, for its flowers are starry in shape when widely expanded, and the inner surface shines as though newly varnished, and is of a greener tint of yellow than is found in any other Crocus, closely approaching that of *Ranunculus Ficaria,* the Lesser Celandine.

The Russian General Korolkov discovered it in Turkestan, and the first forms distributed by Regel, in 1882, are not robust in constitution; the small flowers are stained externally with a faint brown freckling merging into dull green at the throat. I find great difficulty in keeping this form in health and have never obtained seed from it. *C. Korolkowii* was afterwards found on the northern frontier of Afghanistan, and in 1901 was collected in quantity in Bukhara for Messrs. Van Tubergen, of Haarlem. These collected corms were so flat and large that they were thought to be those of some Gladiolus, but when they flowered in 1902 we were delighted with their rich purple and brown markings and the superior vigour of this race. They have since seeded freely and are hardy and free-flowering and, in most seasons, show flowers between Christmas and the New Year.

As might be expected from a Crocus from such an outlying habitat for the genus, *C. Korolkowii* shows many very distinct characters. Thus it has a greater number of leaves than any other spring-flowering species, and the seed capsules, as in *C. caspius,* another Eastern species, do not appear above ground when ripe.

It has a tunic of fine parallel fibres which rise up into a long cap at the summit of the flat corm. The leaves spread out on the ground soon after their appearance, and the flowers are freely produced and very showy, being of such a distinct greenish yellow.

Forms richly marked outside with purple have been selected and listed as the variety *vinosus*; I have raised a pretty sulphur form, and have selected, from collected roots, a very striking variety in which the back of the outer segments is brown with a narrow margin of yellow. It reminded me so much of the handsome water beetle *Dytiscus marginalis* that I named it *Crocus Korolkowii* var. 'Dytiscus.' It reproduces itself fairly truly from seed and seems a vigorous form. *C. Korolkowii* does better here in rather heavy soil than in a dry and sandy position.

C. Suterianus of Herbert was discovered by Henry Suter, British Vice-Consul at Kayseri, and was described by Herbert in the *Botanical Register* in 1845 and figured by him as *C. chrysanthus* (*Bot. Reg.*, t. 4: 1847), the mistake being afterwards explained in his 'History of Crocus,' in *Journ. Hort. Soc.*, London, 2, 285 (1847). The name *C. Aucheri* Boiss. is a synonym for this species.

It is found in central Asia Minor, and but for its isolated habitat and narrower leaves might be regarded as a variety of the European *C. Olivieri*.

It is not common in cultivation, but is so generous, both with its deep yellow flowers and the increase of its corms, that if field mice could be reduced to the status of the Dodo and Great Auk this Crocus might be in every rock garden.

It should be lifted and replanted every third year, or else the corms become crowded into superimposed layers. Such a patch is very attractive when in flower, but the crowd of corms lifted so close to the surface is too great a temptation to a mouse for the safety of the Crocus.

C. Olivieri of J. Gay was named after a French traveller and botanist, Guillaume Antoine Olivier (1756-1814), who was the first to collect it in the island of Chios in the Ægean Sea. It is also found in Greece, Bulgaria and Roumania, and I have received living roots of it from near Salonica. Though a dwarf and small flowered species, with segments only about an inch and a quarter long, it is so free-flowering and of such a brilliant shade of orange as to deserve a good place in the rock garden. In both this and the last species each of the three stigmatic branches are divided into no more than two threadlike divisions. This character easily distinguishes it from the other wide-leaved members of this group, *CC. Balansae* and *candidus*, in which the divisions are more numerous. The leaves are quite a third of an inch in width at maturity, but those of *C. Suterianus* are never wider than a quarter of an inch. *C. Olivieri* usually has only two or three leaves from a sheath. One of the specimens figured on Maw's plate 53 has four leaves, but this is unusual. Maw writes of a difference in the corm tunics, but does not explain it. He also states that the keel of the leaves is ciliated all over in *C. Suterianus* but only on the edge in *C. Olivieri*. I have not found this constant or reliable, and can only divide them according to the width of leaf and certain characters of the flowers that are scarcely distinct enough to be of botanical value, but catch my gardener's eye. I notice that the narrow-leaved forms have more globular, deeper-coloured flowers, with light purple stripes on the perianth tube and a stain of brown or grey at the base of the segments, as in Herbert's figure. My Greek, wide-leaved, true *C. Olivieri* has more pointed segments and no trace of brown or purple on tube or throat. Captain Sowels collected it at Bougiati, near Athens, and I saw it there in 1926, and though I failed to find it there in 1938 I collected it on a hillside between Athens and Thebes.

C. Balansae of J. Gay is found in western Asia Minor near Smyrna, and was named after another French traveller and botanist, Benedict Balansa (1825-91). It may be distinguished at once from *CC. Olivieri, Suterianus* and *candidus* by its earlier flowering and the deep orange stigmata, which are divided into twelve or more fine threads instead of the six only of the others, and from *C. candidus* also by its smooth membranous tunic.

It is very variable in its external markings, but uniformly of a yolk-of-egg yellow within. I have never seen it without some lines, or suffusion of purple or brown on the tube, which markings generally reach to the tips of the outer segments as featherings or freckling. Its most striking form has a complete external suffusion of rich mahogany brown on the outer segments, so dark that brown madder shaded with purple-lake must be used to reproduce it in paint. The flowers are generally less than an inch in length but well formed, with rounded segments, and expand freely on sunny mornings. I always feel that it deserves the adjective 'jolly,' more than other Crocuses, especially when in a half-opened state so that the deep purple-red of the exterior contrasts with the orange within. Other forms are pleasing, especially those with well-marked bronze feathering, but everyone picks out the brown and yellow variety as first favourite. It seeds freely in most seasons and seems to prefer rich and moist soil so long as it is fully exposed to the midday sunshine. The broad leaves are worth examining through a lens on account of the silvery hairs scattered over their upper and under surfaces. It begins to flower early in February and produces a long succession of flowers.

C. candidus of E. D. Clarke inhabits the Troad, the modern Bigha—a vilayet of western Asia Minor. It has been collected on Mount Gargarus, one of the heights of Ida, and in the valley of the Scamander now called the River Mendore. The white form was the first to be described and cultivated, but it is a very variable species, and pale yellow and deep orange forms are now in cultivation, some of which produce both white and yellow seedlings.

The yellow and orange forms are not easy to distinguish by flowers and leaves only from *C. Olivieri* and some varieties of *C. Balansae*, though the leaf of *C. candidus* is generally wider than theirs. The corm tunic, however, comes to the rescue of the puzzled gardener. Nature fortunately designed it in a lighter shade of brown, almost drab when dry, and it generally shows strong ribs of parallel fibres from the base to its sharply pointed cap. Messrs. Van Tubergen raised seedlings at Haarlem, some of which had a yellow ground colour, and distributed them under the name of *C. candidus* var. *sub-flavus*, and two years later I found similar varieties among my seedlings. When looking through Maw's herbarium at the British Museum (Natural History) I recognised a sheet of specimens collected by Sintenis at Thymbra, in the valley of the Scamander, as a yellow form of *C. candidus*. As hitherto it had only been known in the white form they had been placed among the unrecognised species. In 1911 Mr. Mountain, of San Stefano, Constantinople, sent Messrs. Barr a few collected bulbs from a district 'some

50 to 60 miles from Mount Olympus.' The Bithynian Olympus is about 150 miles from the valley of the Scamander, but a collector does not always give the exact distances and localities to those who seek plants as well as knowledge. When these flowered they proved a fine, deep orange form of *C. candidus*, which has been listed as var. *Mountainii*. It seems to me that Herbert's *C. lagenaeflorus* var. 8, *Landerianus*, from Kurchumlu Tepe in the Troad, with orange or yellow flowers includes these forms and they should be called *C. candidus* var. *Landerianus*.

In cultivation *C. candidus* flowers among the latest Crocuses, and in cool ground continues to the end of March and in late seasons into April. The wide leaves and freely produced flowers make it a very attractive and distinct plant for borders and the rock garden, and where weeding and hoeing are not too assiduously practised it will sow itself freely. Whether the ground colour is white or yellow the outside of the flowers is generally freckled and veined with blue, purple or brown, in endless variety. A cream-coloured form that has appeared here is one of the most floriferous of all Crocuses. I suspect *C. candidus* of hybridising with other species, having found its characteristic strongly ribbed tunic on certain chance seedlings whose origin I cannot otherwise explain.

C. vitellinus of Wahlenberg is plentiful in Syria, near Beirut, on Lebanon, at Scanderun and near Saida. It is reported from North Syria, near Aleppo, and even in the Cilician Taurus, but these latter records may refer to *C. graveolens*.

The southern plant is the best and bears fragrant deep yellow flowers from mid-December onward. The segments are narrow and pointed, and as it is the only orange-flowered species with much divided stigmata which flowers at that period it is easily recognised. The tunic is smooth and of a reddish brown, splitting, at the lower edge only, into a fringe of narrow points. The leaves appear before the flowers and are narrow with ciliated edges to the blades and keel.

The outer segments are marked with dark bronze stripes in some forms, but the ground colour should be as rich and bright as the inner surface, and the throat should taper gradually down to the tube.

Forms have been found in which the anthers are black like

those of *C. hyemalis* var. *Foxii*; most of these had dark bronze featherings or stripes on the outer segments and so belong to the variety *syriacus* described and figured by Baker in t. 6416 (1879) of the *Botanical Magazine*.

He wrote 'orange-yellow, its oblong spathulate segments concolorous in the original *vitellinus*; striped with five feathered lines down the back in the variety *syriacus*.'

Unfortunately the numeral 3 on the fine plate has been used instead of 'fig. 1' in the reference to '*tab. nostra*' following var. *syriacus* in the synonymy, but is correctly used in the explanation of the plate at the end.

C. graveolens of Boissier and Reuter has been treated by Baker and Maw as though it were only a variety of *C. vitellinus* with brown markings, and has been collected and distributed of late years under that name. Boissier described it as having narrower leaves that spread on the ground, and longer proper spathes reaching to the throat instead of ending below it. He lays stress on the way the flower opens out into a flat star instead of remaining bell-shaped, and also on its heavy odour, like that of Elder. He gives Gebel Nahas, near Aleppo, and Beilan as its habitat, and it seems likely that *C. graveolens* is the more northern and *C. vitellinus* the southern plant.

As I know it in cultivation it is quite distinct from *C. vitellinus*. The two are not in flower together, as *C. graveolens* is never earlier than mid-February. The throat swells out considerably above the tube and there is a very noticeable waist or constriction in the lower third of the flower, while in *C. vitellinus* the segments taper gradually to the throat. The stellate manner of opening noted by Boissier is very marked as the segments open out from above the waist very freely on sunny days. The outer segments are generally paler on the outer than the inner surface and many are striped or feathered with brown, but forms in which the outer surface is of a plain straw colour are not uncommon. *C. graveolens* would however be recognisable anywhere without these characters by the abominable odour that is perceptible, even at a distance of some yards, when its small flowers are open on a sunny day. Boissier flattered it by the mild name *graveolens* and comparing its scent with Elder. It reminds me of the horrible odour of *Cytisus purgans*, that has unfortunately

descended to its hybrid offspring *C.* × *praecox* and *C.* × *kewensis*.
The Crocus has an added whiff of black-beetles as well, and in
most seasons the first indication I receive of its being in flower is
this pungent odour, which reaches my nose before the yellow
of the flower catches my eye.

Dried specimens retain this scent for many years, and it even
defiles the paper in which they have been pressed, in much the
same way as Petrel eggs scent the drawer in which they are kept.

Three yellow-flowered species have been described since the
first edition of this book (1924) and may be conveniently dealt
with here. They can be distinguished as follows:

1. { Flowers with purple throat.   *C. scardicus.*
   { Flowers wholly yellow.   2.

2. { Tunic finely reticulate.   *C. Cvijicii.*
   { Tunic hard and shining, breaking up
   {   at base into parallel fibres.   *C. Sieheanus.*

C. Cvijicii of Košanin was described and illustrated in
Glas. Srp. Kraljevske Akademije, Beograd, 119, 23, t. 2, in 1926.
It was named in honour of Professor Joran Cvijić, whom
Košanin described as the most illustrious authority on the
geography and geology of Macedonia. I have never discovered
how this name should be pronounced, whether it is better to
imitate a sneeze or, as a witty friend of mine put it, 'to play it
on the violin.' I am afraid very few gardeners need to practise
for the accomplishment, as although a good supply of corms
was collected by Mr. W. Th. Ingwersen in Albania in 1937 it
is still a great rarity in English gardens. *Crocus Cvijicii* had a
very small corm, always a bad sign, which suggests that
increase is chiefly by seed. The tunic is composed of very
slender reticulated fibres, in which character it differs from
C. ancyrensis, in which the netted tunic fibres are coarse. The
proper spathe is diphyllous and the flowers solitary. Mr.
Ingwersen in a letter to me described the colour of the flowers,
'mostly a rich clear yellow, but a few even when newly opened
appeared to be almost silvery lemon colour.' Although closely
allied in general characters to *C. veluchensis* its yellow flowers
distinguish it at a glance from the lilac or white forms of
C. veluchensis.

It is a vernal species, flowering as soon as the snow melts

in July in the mountains of Serbian Macedonia. In England it flowers in February or March.

The specimens described by Košanin were collected by Dr. Lj. Glisic on Mount Galičice, and Mr. Ingwersen found it 'just under the topmost pinnacle cliffs of Mount Ostrovitza, blooming in great drifts along the edges of the last, melting snowdrifts.' He mentions that it was not easy to extract the corms from the stony ground still frozen an inch below the surface.

C. scardicus of Košanin was described and illustrated in the same journal as *C. Cvijicii*, from which it differs chiefly in the presence of a basal spathe and a violet or lilac throat combined with its yellow flowers. It was found on Mount Skardo flowering in July and August following the melting of the snow. So far as I know it has not been introduced into cultivation. A Crocus with such a remarkable combination of colours would be an exceedingly interesting introduction to our gardens. The original descriptions and figures of *CC. Cvijicii* and *C. scardicus* were reprinted in 1928 in a paper by Košanin on the Crocuses of southern Serbia published in *Bulletin de l'Institut et du Jardin Botaniques, Beograd,* 1, pp. 91-5 (1928).

Crocus Sieheanus of B. L. Burtt is another newcomer and was described and figured in the *Botanical Magazine,* vol. 162, t. 9583 (1939).

It was discovered by W. Siehe in the Taurus Mountains of Asia Minor, and corms were collected in 1927 and sent to Messrs. Barr, who with their usual generosity sent some to me.

When they flowered in 1929 I found that they differed from all the yellow-flowered species I knew in several characters, especially from *C. ancyrensis* in their smooth tunic splitting into strong parallel fibres at the base—as against the reticulated fibre of *C. ancyrensis*; and from *C. aureus* in the scarlet colour of the stigmata. So I reported to Messrs. Barr that it should be regarded as a new species, and suggested its being named *C. Sieheanus* in honour of its discoverer. The colour of its flowers is not such a glowing orange tone as that of *C. aureus,* nor are they so large and well shaped, and a little too starry to gain top marks as a garden plant, though to the botanist it is of great interest, especially as a large proportion of corms produce flowers with black barbs in the anthers. This is such a marked feature of most varieties of *C. chrysanthus* that taken together with the smooth tunic it suggests the possibility of *C. Sieheanus* being a hybrid between *CC. ancyrensis* and *chrysanthus* if those two species occur together somewhere in Asia Minor. At present we know too little about them to do more than suspect a parentage.

Unfortunately it has never been a strong grower, and both here and with Mr. Barr it seems to have been one of the casualties of the war years.

XI

Annulate Crocuses

THE Annulate Crocuses form a group in which the lowest third of the corm tunic splits into a series of narrow rings that just overlap each other, and although generally straight-edged below are armed upwards with stiff teeth that assist one ring to adhere to another. Two species, *C. pulchellus* and *C. speciosus*, flower in autumn and are dealt with under another section.

Some species are difficult to distinguish clearly, on account of their great range of variation in shape and colour and their capacity for crossing with one another.

George Maw thought it likely that *C. aërius* and *C. chrysanthus* hybridised when growing intermixed on the Bithynian Olympus, and they most certainly do so in gardens as well as with some varieties of *C. biflorus*. This makes it impossible to draw a sharp line between these three species, and the following key will only apply to the more characteristic forms of this bewildering trio.

Spring-flowering annulate species:

1. { Tunic thick and hard. — 2.
   { Tunic thin and papery. — 6.

2. { Flowers tapering downwards gradually
        without a distinct waist. — 3.
   { Flowers generally with a distinct waist. — 5.

3. { Anthers black. — *C. Crewei.*
   { Anthers yellow. — 4.

4. { Filaments spotted with black at the base. — *C. Pestalozzae.*
   { Filaments and anthers without black
        spots. — *C. biflorus.*

5. { Anthers with grey centres. — *C. isauricus.*
   { Anthers generally with black barbs. — *C. chrysanthus.*

6. { Filaments yellow. — 7.
   { Filaments scarlet. — 8.

7. { Flowers globose with a distinct waist. — *C. aërius.*
   { Flowers long without a waist. — *C. tauri.*

8. {
  Flowers small, proper spathe mono-
phyllous, rings of tunic without teeth. *C. cyprius.*
  Flowers longer, proper spathe diphyl-
lous, rings of tunic armed with
strong teeth.   *C. Hartmannianus.*

C. biflorus was so named by Miller in the eighth edition (1768) of that marvellous example of one man's work, *The Gardener's Dictionary.* He distinguishes it thus—'Crocus with two flowers in each spatha.' We find, however, in his further description that he uses the term spatha loosely, sometimes correctly for the proper spathes, but also for what should be termed the sheathing scales. So he writes of *C. biflorus*—'with a few narrow leaves which are closely wrapped round by a spatha or sheath, out of which arise two flowers.' This plainly refers to the sheathing scales and could be said of the greater number of species; but we must bear in mind that Miller was comparing a free-flowering form of *C. biflorus* with the Saffron Crocus and what is in part *C. nudiflorus,* and some forms of *C. susianus,* none of which are so free flowering.

C. biflorus as generally grown is an old garden form, called the Scotch Crocus, which most likely originated as a seedling in some Scottish garden and was introduced from thence into England and Holland. Nothing very closely resembling it has been found in a wild state, and like other old garden varieties it is sterile and increases rapidly by corm division.

It has larger flowers than other striped varieties of *C. biflorus,* a yellow throat, white ground colour, with five more or less feathered blue-purple stripes on the outside of the outer segments. It is well figured in t. 845 (1805) of the *Botanical Magazine,* which clearly shows its very characteristic brown spathes. Such a hardy, early and free-flowering variety deserves planting in large groups, where its white flowers can open out in the morning sunshine. It has no fads as to soil so long as it is not waterlogged.

Var. *Parkinsonii* of Sabine is var. *lineatus* of Herbert. A smaller variety, with rounder flowers and a similarly obliging habit, is offered by nurserymen as *praecox, argenteus* or under a combination of those two names.

It may be further distinguished from the large variety by a

shade of creamy-buff on the outside of the outer segments, which moreover have only three instead of five conspicuous stripes. It is pure white within with a rich orange throat and conspicuous scarlet stigmata.

Sabine in his paper in the *Transactions of the Horticultural Society* for 1830 figures this form as *C. biflorus Parkinsonii*, seeing in it the *C. Vernus Striatus Vulgaris* of Parkinson's *Paradisus*. It is not unlikely that it was the parent from which the Scotch Crocus was derived after Parkinson's day.

Var. *argenteus*. Sabine's *argenteus* and the seedling he raised from it and called *argenteus praecox*, figured in his plate as No. 5, are not often found in gardens but seem to me to be forms of the wild variety found plentifully round Florence and in other parts of Italy.

Their distinguishing features are described by Sabine and Herbert as narrower segments, pale lilac within, and with three purple lines on the outside of the outer ones.

Near Florence it varies, and a form without stripes on the outer segments is known as the variety *estriatus* and is a charming plant for the rock garden. The creamy-yellow exterior of the outer segments is very pleasing in contrast with the soft lilac of the rest of the blossom and it is curious in flowering much earlier than the striped form. I have raised seedlings from it, and though a large proportion reproduce the variety *estriatus* I obtained about five per cent. of the striped later-flowering form, and in some batches of seedlings one or two of a beautiful little albino, pure white except for the band of straw colour on the outer segments. If self-fertilised this white form breeds true and is valuable for the rock garden as it flowers latest of all the varieties of *C. biflorus*.

This sequence in flowering has been perfectly regular ever since I have grown these varieties and is a very curious fact seeing that all three are but forms of one.

It is very difficult to reconcile the views of Herbert, Sabine and other writers as to the *C. pusillus* of Tenore and its varieties. Herbert treats it as variety 6 of his *C. annulatus*, of which he makes *biflorus* the variety 1.

Herbert places *argenteus* as sub-variety 2 of *pusillus*. His description clearly fits the wild Italian plant which I find produces the variety *estriatus*. Though it is difficult to say exactly what Tenore and other writers have included under the name it seems best to retain it for a small, starry-flowered Italian race of *C. biflorus*. That sold by nurserymen as *pusillus* is generally white in ground colour, with a faint tint of buff and three to five narrow, purple lines on the outer segments.

This must be the 'smallest with the clearest white ground' that Herbert says is found at St. Rocco, near Naples, and which he calls sub-variety *Tenoreanus*.

The smaller varieties from Naples with the blue tint mentioned by Herbert may be a form that I bought as the variety *minor*, and was the same as the form naturalised in Barton Park, Suffolk, and figured by Haworth in *English Botany, Supplement*, No. 2645, which is the original of the plate 1497 in the third edition of Sowerby's *English Botany*, vol. 9 (1883).

Whittall sent to Kew some small forms collected near Smyrna, thought to represent Herbert's variety *nubigenus*. They varied greatly in external markings and some were closely akin to *pusillus*. They have poor constitutions and are likely to die out in cultivation.

Var. *Weldenii* is the Dalmatian form and an altogether bolder and more beautiful plant than the Italian varieties. It ranges eastward into Serbia and Bulgaria and varies from pure white within and without, Herbert's variety 5 *albus*, through forms with a light freckling of blue on the outer segments, to extreme forms in which the entire outer surface, except a narrow white margin, is of a deep lustrous purple, and then becomes the variety *Alexandri* figured in t. 7740 (1900) of the *Botanical Magazine*. This handsome form was described by Herbert as variety 4 *purpurascens*, and his plants were sent to him from Dalmatia, but those collected of later years are from Serbia and Bulgaria. Among the collected forms are some with poor star-shaped flowers, and others with blue freckling or feathering replacing the rich purple, and I can see no definite dividing line between the varieties *Weldenii* and *Alexandri*. Both make splendid garden plants, flowering rather late in February and on till March, the large glistening white flowers looking especially beautiful when half opened so that the outer segments show the various shades of lilac or purple of their markings. The flower is more gourd-shaped than in other forms of *C. biflorus*, and the throat is never at all yellow but always pure white. It is a free seeder and crosses easily with *C. chrysanthus*, producing very beautiful forms with sulphur and primrose-yellow ground colour, more or less marked with blue outside. The characteristic black-barbed anthers of *C. chrysanthus* generally appear in these forms, and one of the best was shown by Messrs. Barr in 1915, obtaining an Award of Merit as *C. chrysanthus* var. 'Lemon Queen.'

There remains a range of forms with ground colouring of shades of lilac and almost blue, more pronounced than in the variety *estriatus*, the deepest coloured of the Italian forms. They are the most Eastern forms of this widespread species, and have been collected in the Cilician Taurus, Circassia, round Tiflis and even in the mountains of N.W. Persia.

C. Adami of J. Gay was turned by Herbert into his *C. annulatus* var. *Adamicus*, to cover these blue-grounded forms; the name *C. biflorus* var. *Adamicus* is correct, although Baker's combination *C. biflorus* var. *Adami* has been frequently used.

Being so remarkably variable they will need further sub-division as they become better known, but at present they are very scarce in cultivation.

The lilac form with rich featherings outside figured in t. 3868 (1841) of the *Botanical Magazine* from Herbert's drawing is unlike any I have seen in having a white margin to the outer segments and being a much larger plant.

Messrs. Van Tubergen received a consignment from the Caucasus in 1902, and I saw the collected dried specimens and flowered others here. They varied greatly, but mostly had a buff, more or less feathered exterior to the outer segments, being otherwise of a rosy lilac. They are delicate in constitution, and the few that I have kept alive have been saved by the protection of a frame. One among them had a thinner tunic and richer purple shades in the flower. In general appearance they resembled *C. corsicus*, but the rings of the hard, plain tunic show their true affinity.

In 1907 Mr. Barr kindly sent me two corms collected, I believe, in the Cilician Taurus, one of which has increased fairly well and seems to be the second form of *C. Adami* known to Herbert, of which he writes 'the other is of a bluer tint than any Crocus I have seen.'

At the time of flowering the leaves are curiously grey and upright and serve to set off the extraordinary blueness of the outside of the flowers a tint nearly approaching real blue. The flowers are so unresponsive to sunlight that they only open on very fine and warm mornings, often remaining tightly closed when varieties of *C. chrysanthus* growing alongside are widely opened. However, they look their best when closed, for the inner segments are of a pale bluish lavender. So far it has never borne seeds here, doubtless because it so seldom opens, so I know only the one form derived from one collected corm, as the other failed to grow. The unusual colour catches one's eye from a great distance, and flowering as it does early in February it would be a great acquisition to the garden should it some day become plentiful.

In 1901 I found a self-sown seedling in the rock garden, unlike anything else. It appears to be an extreme form of the variety *Weldenii* with the whole flower tinted with lilac. The segments are bold and rounded, the outer ones nearly covered with purple featherings. There is just a trace of yellow in the throat that may denote a hybrid origin, perhaps a cross with a blue *C. chrysanthus* or *C. aërius*. It possesses a good constitution. Had it been a wild plant from the Caucasus I should have referred it to *C. Adami*, but think it best, being assured of its garden origin, to call it Blue *biflorus*. Seedlings that I have since raised show distinct traces of *C. aërius* and are very close to the beautiful strain raised by Mr. T. Smith, of Newry, and named by him *C. aërius* 'Celeste.' These, judging by the size of the flowers and the hard coriaceous corm tunic, seem to me to have a good deal of *C. biflorus* var. *Weldenii* in their pedigree.

C. biflorus var. *Barrii* was first noticed by me at a fortnightly show of the Royal Horticultural Society, as an unusually closely feathered form of the white-grounded variety *pusillus* with which it was shown. As I grew it here I found it a very remarkable form and that the leaves pierce through the ground in tufts and spread out on the surface, looking much like clumps of that omnipresent weed *Poa annua*. They are, moreover, of a very bright yellow-green like that grass. It flowers later than other forms of *C. biflorus*, except the albino, and so freely that the flowers actually prevent one another from opening fully. The corm tunic is thinner in texture than that of an ordinary *C. biflorus*, and the membrane is mixed with parallel fibre and splits at the base.

C. isauricus is the name attached to a rather variable plant collected in 1907 by Siehe. Isauria is the classical name for a district of Galatia with a city called Isaura and afterwards Claudiopolis. So presumably this Crocus comes from the Cilician Taurus somewhere near the modern town of Ermenek. It may be the variety of *C. biflorus* mentioned by Maw as found there by Mrs. Danford.

As I know it in the garden it suggests a close affinity with *C. chrysanthus* in the gourd-shaped flowers with rounded segments, but it has a few characters that are distinct. The broad anthers generally show a white central band before dehiscence, and in most specimens there is a slight shading of grey or even a black line by the edge of the pollen sacs. The leaves are of a remarkably pale grey-green, very similar to those of the strangely blue form of *C. Adami* described above. The flowers have a white ground and a yellow throat and are variously freckled, or finely feathered outside with bluish grey or dull purple. The scarlet stigmata give a pleasant touch of colour to an otherwise rather dowdy flower. Some have a strong scent like heather honey, or *Lobularia maritima*, in others quite an unpleasant tang is mixed with the scent. A hard coriaceous tunic, with distinct rings at the base, and diphyllous proper spathes are characters common to both *C. biflorus* and *C. chrysanthus* as well as to this plant, which, if it reproduces itself truly from seed, may be regarded as a species intermediate between the two older ones.

C. chrysanthus of Herbert was named from a dried specimen collected by Frivaldsky on the Rhodope Mountains, Bulgaria. It is the most variable species known as regards colour, the ground colour being sulphur yellow, orange, white or lilac, while the outer segments show every imaginable degree of freckling, suffusion and feathering of chocolate, brown, grey or purple, or they may be self-coloured. Some of the white forms with blue markings are difficult to distinguish from small forms of *C. biflorus* and have been confused with it. The most reliable characters are the golden throat of *C. chrysanthus*, together with its rounder, more gourd-shaped flower. Nature has fortunately vouchsafed a special aid to the puzzled gardener in providing black tips to the barbs of the anthers in the greater number of forms of *C. chrysanthus* but withholding them altogether from all forms of *C. biflorus*. These black barbs may be wanting in some specimens and there is a starry-flowered race of *C. chrysanthus* in which the anthers are more or less suffused with a smoky brown, and the flowers striped or freckled with dull grey or brown on the outer segments. Baker placed these as the varieties *fusco-lineatus* and *fusco-tinctus* of *C. chrysanthus*. If their geographical range were limited and isolated, I should feel inclined to regard them as, at any rate, a sub-species, as their shape, fuscous anthers and pale yellow stigmata are such constantly co-related characters. They are the least attractive varieties of this showy species. The other forms may be recognised as *C. chrysanthus* at sight, be they white, blue or yellow, if the black barbs are present on the anthers.

This species occurs in Asia Minor, e.g. near Smyrna and on the Bithynian Olympus, and in Greece, e.g. in the Cephalonian fir forest above Delphi, on Parnassus, and near Tripolis in the Peloponnese. It is very hardy and one of the earliest of flowers in the New Year. Owing to its variability it is also one of the most interesting from which to raise seedlings.

The type as described by Herbert is a rich orange-yellow and of good globular outline, very free flowering, each set of sheathing leaves producing a succession of three, four or more flowers, and three such sets may arise from one strong corm. From the type I have raised forms with yellow ground beautifully feathered outside, one of which has been widely distributed as 'Yellow Hammer.' A larger and more richly feathered form I call 'Golden Pheasant,' which is No. 5 on Plate 23. 'Snow Bunting,' and 'Golden Plover' are other striped seedlings raised here, and are growing on into stocks. It will be noticed that I choose the names of birds as far as possible for my seedlings of *C. chrysanthus* and *C. biflorus*.

A yellow form with a purplish-grey throat and tube has produced a strain in which the outer segments are more or less suffused with purple or brown. 'Bumble-bee' so aptly described one in which, when half open, the yellow inner segments look like the golden bands on the body of a large bumble-bee that it bears the name of the insect instead of that of a bird.

The best seedlings of all were raised by Messrs. Van Tubergen from a pale sulphur, large-flowered form known as the variety *pallidus*. Many of these are twice as large as ordinary *C. chrysanthus* and very robust. Perhaps the best of them is shown in Plate 22. I admired it so much when I first saw the blossoms Mr. Hoog sent me from Haarlem that he kindly sent me corms and named it after me. I am very proud of my namesake, although I did not raise it, as it has done so well here, and its butter-coloured, rounded blooms are singled out from some distance by all who see them as one of the most charming. A set of its sister seedlings generously given to me by their raiser have also done well. If only it would increase more rapidly the handsomest of them, a sulphur with rich purple bands on the outer segments, fig. iii, in Plate 23, would be widely known. This I named, by consent of its raiser, 'John Hoog.' 'Moonlight' made its début at a meeting at Vincent Square, and was given an Award of Merit. In this the sulphur yellow fades to a pale cream at the tips of the segments and the massed flowers in the bed have a delightfully pale moonlight effect.

Maw shows a figure of a pure white form with yellow throat, and apparently no trace of grey or purple at the base of the segments. I have no form so good as this, but in some the markings are very pale and small, and I still hope for the day when a pure white exterior will be found on a new seedling. White forms with blue featherings or stripes are numerous. 'Snow Bunting' is my best, and is fig. ii on Plate 23. It received a F.C.C. in 1925.

Another strain with white ground I raised from a small feathered form that came to me as *C. biflorus nubigenus*. It has conspicuous black barbs on the anthers and so golden a throat that I ought to have guessed that it was a form of *C. chrysanthus* before seeing its seedlings.

They all showed so much yellow on the outside of the outer segments that there was then no doubt, and when examining Maw's herbarium in the British Museum I found a sheet of

specimens labelled '*nubigenus*,' some of which were identical
with the one I grew under that name. They came from
Chamlijah, above Scutari, and are mentioned in Maw's
monograph and two are figured in rather dim colouring in his
Plate 59*b*, fig. 3. The enlarged anthers show a slight shading
for the black barb, but though one or two show no trace
of it, most of his dried specimens have it very strongly
developed. Its presence or absence also occurs in my sets of
seedlings.

The best of these seedlings is my 'Bullfinch,' a remarkably
round flower, creamy yellow, richly feathered with crimson-
purple outside, pure white within but for its orange throat.
This is the subject of Plate 23, but slightly reduced in size.

'Siskin' has a more pointed flower, bright yellow freckled
with grey on the outer segments, a cheery, free-flowering but
small form. I hope for a seedling in which the three outer
segments will be rich yellow without and the inner segments
and all the interior white, but so far none has appeared quite
free from the grey basal marking.

Maw seems to have known no form with a blue ground to
the interior, his variety *coerulescens* being described as white,
marked outside with purple and bluish lilac. Seeds saved from
the white forms produce many that should be ranged under
this variety *coerulescens*. One of the finest was raised by Mr.
Hoog from the variety *pallidus* and gained an Award of Merit
when shown in London as 'Warley Variety,' and is now known
as 'Warley White.' It is a handsome form, rather like 'Bullfinch' in general colouring, but the flower is longer and there
is more blue in its purple suffusion.

It seeds fairly truly, but occasionally gives a sulphur seedling
like its parent.

Others are so large and so much like *C. biflorus Alexandri* that
I believe they show evidence of ancestral unions with its richly
coloured forms. One that I called 'Blue Throat,' after that rare
little bird, is the best of them.

The latest development of this strain has been named 'Blue
Peter' by its raiser, Mr. Thomas Hoog. In its fine globular
shape it resembles *C. aërius major* and 'Bullfinch,' but the
rounded segments are pure white within with a suffusion of

rich purple on the backs of the three outer ones. These, more-over, have such a remarkably glossy surface that it shows a band of reflected light as if from a polished gem instead of a flower.

It is possible that the many seedlings now appearing here with a blue-lilac ground colour have a trace of *C. aërius* in them, but the hard tunic, black-spotted anthers and early-flowering habit show that most of them are best ranged under *C. chrysanthus*. My first blue form, and still one of the best, I call 'Blue Rock.' Its outer segments have deep purple shading at the throat on the lilac ground.

Another strain with a blending of yellow and lilac in them, the general effect of which is rather dull and mustardy, I class as 'Khaki.' Those of a creamy yellow shaded at the edge or flushed with rosy lilac I class as 'Shot,' and the very pale ones with a wash of cream and lilac on a white ground as 'Opal.'

These, and a race with a pale sulphur or cream ground, plain or freckled with lilac, are the latest breaks in this variable species, and suggest a cross with *C. biflorus Weldenii*.

C. aërius of Herbert is a close relative of *C. chrysanthus* and hybridises with it in gardens. Both grow on the Bithynian Olympus, and there is no constant character beyond the much thinner, papery tunic and later-flowering habit of *C. aërius* to separate them.

All the wild forms I have seen are blue in ground colour, but though Herbert described his variety *stauricus* as white and lilac inside he saw dried specimens only, which may have been Maw's variety *coerulescens* of *C. chrysanthus*.

The charm of *C. aërius* lies in the rich crimson or purple markings on the outer segments and its beautifully globular form. It is not a very robust species and is apt to die out, but fortunately it seeds freely and its bright red seeds are pleasantly conspicuous and easy to collect even though shed from the capsules. A very fine form known as *C. aërius major* was raised at Newry with flowers twice as large as in the type and beautifully shaded with blue and crimson. It, too, is not easy to keep, and seedlings vary a good deal. A curious form with yellow ground and brown and grey markings appears among seedlings where *C. chrysanthus* is grown as a neighbour, and generally shows its hybrid origin by having black and brown markings of varying intensity on the barbs of the anthers. Certain greyish and pale lilac forms I believe to be hybrids with *C. biflorus*; the best of them all is the variety 'Celeste' that originated at Newry and is mentioned above under *C. biflorus*.

C. cyprius of Boissier and Kotschy is a diminutive species peculiar to Cyprus. It is rather delicate, but so beautiful that it is worth protecting in a frame or under a hand-light. The flowers are a soft lavender, with very rich orange throat and deep purple blotches at the base of the segments externally. Among collected corms I found a very pretty form with a white ground colour which showed up the external purple markings very effectively, but regret to add that it has disappeared. However, visitors to Cyprus might find others and be more successful with them. The type is fairly plentiful in Troodos; a healthy corm of the white sent to me would be a very pleasing commission in return for this hint.

Its distinguishing characters are the bright scarlet of its filaments, a soft membranous tunic that splits into rings without teeth at the base, and a monophyllous proper spathe.

The filament distinguishes it from *C. aërius*, and its monophyllous spathe and absence of teeth on the rings of the tunic from *C. Hartmannianus*, which was described as a new species in 1914 and named after a German botanist, Ernst Hartmann.

I noticed *C. Hartmannianus* of Holmboe among collected plants of *C. cyprius* from Mount Troodos in 1904 and again in 1909 at shows of the Royal Horticultural Society, and have managed to keep the two forms alive in a cold frame. The two individuals I thus obtained vary somewhat in the colouring of their flowers, but both are paler in ground tint than *C. cyprius* and have the purple markings of the outer segments continued farther up towards the tip.

In the first of these the anthers are tinged with brown at their tips, in the other they are jet black, but both have scarlet filaments like those of *C. cyprius*.

The corm tunic is a stiffish membrane with parallel fibres running throughout its length, and there are two rings at the base with strong fibrous teeth springing from the upper edges, quite unlike those of any other annulate Crocus.

It is found on the southern slopes of Kionia in open places in the forest above the monastery of Makhaeras about 880 metres above sea-level and flowers in mid-February. Many collectors have secured good stocks of this beautiful species, and it is likely to be a suitable plant for the Alpine house.

Among a few seedlings I have raised, one is larger and more robust and looks as though crossed with *C. chrysanthus*.

C. Pestalozzae was described as a species by Boissier, being named in honour of an Italian doctor, Fortunato Pestalozza, who botanised in Turkey and Syria between 1830 and 1850, but Maw considered it an albino form of Herbert's *C. biflorus* var. *nubigenus*, on the strength of finding it near Constantinople, mingled with a feathered form similar to that he collected on Chamlijah. I have shown that this last is a form of *C. chrysanthus*, and that Maw did not discover its identity. Whether or no the feathered form from Constantinople and that from Chamlijah are identical I am convinced that *C. Pestalozzae* deserves specific rank.

The white-flowered plant figured by Maw on Plate *59b*, fig. 4, was the only form known to him and at that time in cultivation.

In 1929 corms of a Crocus collected near Constantinople were sent to Mr. John Hoog, of Haarlem, and to Messrs. Barr which in the following spring produced slender blue-lilac flowers unlike any we know.

Both of these Crocus experts were puzzled by them and they sent specimens to me. Mr. Hoog's arrived first, but as I was at Nice that March they were forwarded back to the Continent, and after so many days in the post were very dry but had retained their colour.

By soaking and opening out the specimens I was able to recognise two very definite characters which I had observed in the white *C. Pestalozzae* I had grown here. The thread-like style branches distinguish them from any form of *C. chrysanthus*, and a small black spot on the lower, internal portion of the filaments is a character that I have seen in no other Crocus. These minute black specks at a first glance look like tiny pellets of soil fallen into the throat of the flower.

Corms kindly given to me that autumn flowered well in 1931,

when I was able to verify my observations and decide that we now have the blue form of *C. Pestalozzae* as well as the white, and the new arrival is listed as var. *coerulescens*.

It seeds freely, and only once have I found a white seedling. Mr. Barr very kindly sent me the only white one he found among a large stock of collected corms of the blue, so it would appear that the blue form is normal and the white a less common one.

C. Crewei presents the botanical worker with a puzzle that perhaps only the collection of fresh, living material can solve. Sir Joseph Hooker first described a plant under the name in 1875 in the *Botanical Magazine*, t. 6168. The figure and description lead us to believe that the basal rings of an annulate Crocus were not present, and that the tunic resembled that of *C. laevigatus* in splitting towards the base. The successive layers of tunics shown in the figure are those of at least four successive seasons, and had they been cleared away it is likely that the innermost tunic formed in the previous autumn might have shown basal rings.

The white flowers feathered with purple and the black anthers are the same as shown in Maw's Plate LX, and both were drawn from plants collected by Mr. H. J. Elwes on the hills behind Syra. Maw noticed and figured the basal rings, as he knew that it was best to remove tunics of all but the last season's growth.

This form with a white ground was grown by Mr. Smith, of Newry, and I had it from him, but it died out with both of us. I had believed that it flowered in spring, judging by the records in Maw's text, and was greatly surprised when its black anthers proclaimed its identity one autumn among a patch of *C. chrysanthus* collected in the Peloponnese and kindly sent to me by Captain Sowells. In 1938 Major Pam and I found it in open spaces in the woods above Tripolis, where it was growing among the far more plentiful *C. chrysanthus*, but could be distinguished in March by the nearly ripe seed pods, while those of *C. chrysanthus* were still underground. It is very abundant between Tripolis and Sparta, and several friends have told me that it carpeted much of the arable ground with its fragrant white flowers through November and December.

As they were doing war work then, never a corm was collected for me.

I find it too tender here for outside success, but it has thriven, increased and seeded in a frame at Wormley Bury.

The plant generally offered of late years as *C. Crewei* is quite different, more starry in shape and has an internal ground colour that is a clear lilac, and so much like that of *C. reticulatus* that but for the black anthers and annulate tunic of this so-called *C. Crewei*, it would be difficult to distinguish them. I have been unable to find out exactly where it was collected, but my original plants were given me from Kew and sent there by Edward Whittall, of Smyrna.

They grow happily and flower freely in February in the open ground and are very attractive on account of their deep black anthers. I have raised this lilac form quite truly from seed and feel very doubtful about it being a lilac form of the true *C. Crewei*.

C. tauri was described and figured in Maw's monograph, Plate 61, from dried specimens, as no plant exactly agreeing with them has yet been in cultivation. Many plants have been sent from the East under the name, most of which proved to be forms of *C. reticulatus*. One collected by Egger, of Jaffa, is the remarkable vinous purple autumnal species described above as *C. dispathaceus*. Another, from Siehe, of Mersina, is the beautiful blue form I take to be Herbert's blue *C. Adamicus*, and yet another was described by Baker as *C. tauri* var. *melanthorus*, and is so distinct I consider it worthy of specific rank. It is described on page 133. The true *C. tauri* should have a thin, papery corm tunic splitting into rings at the base, which distinguishes it from all forms of *C. biflorus* in which the tunic is thick and hard. Its very short, pale yellow pistil and long wholly lilac flowers distinguish it from *C. aërius*, which closely resembles it in tunic. It was discovered by Aucher-Eloy near the Cilician Gates of the Taurus.

Mr. E. K. Balls on his 1935 expedition to south-east Asia Minor collected a good stock of a Crocus near Gaziantep, near Marash, which comes sufficiently close to Maw's plant to be accorded the name *C. tauri*. It is evidently a very variable species and is not always self-coloured as was the type specimen.

The anthers are usually marked by a thin black line down the inner edge of each flange.

According to Mr. B. L. Burtt one sheet of Balls's dried specimens (No. 918 in Herb. Kew) contains concolorous flowers, but plants of his No. 2158 are variously marked; some have a purple patch at the base of the outer segments, while in others there are purple lines which reach to the tip of the segments; in some the whole of the outer surface is suffused with purple. Balls's specimens seem to have a stronger, harder tunic than Maw's type-specimen.

C. Danfordiae was described by Maw from specimens gathered by Mrs. Danford at Tapizite in the Anti-Taurus and grown by him at Benthall, near Broseley. Although it seeded freely there it was later lost to cultivation, until in 1926 one of Siehe's collectors in Cilicia obtained a large stock and described it as having blue flowers. Siehe therefore thought that it would be *C. tauri*, and distributed it to his Dutch and English clients under that name. When they flowered in February 1927 they were recognised as *C. Danfordiae*.

It is the smallest-flowered Crocus in cultivation, as the still smaller *C. parviflorus*, another of Mrs. Danford's discoveries, has not been introduced.

In all characters except size it closely resembles *C. chrysanthus*, and like that varies in its range of colour from pale primrose yellow to orange, white and pale lilac, some having brown or grey suffusions on the backs of the outer segments, and there is generally a trace of black on the barbs of the anthers. The shortness of the stigmata selected by Maw as the principal distinction and its occurrence farther to the east of Asia Minor than the range of *C. chrysanthus* entitle *C. Danfordiae* to rank as a species instead of as a minor variety of *C. chrysanthus*.

As the flowers are less than three-quarters of an inch in length it is a botanical curiosity rather than a decorative plant.

XII

Miscellaneous Spring-Flowering Species

THIS chapter contains certain species that do not fit in conveniently with those already grouped, but otherwise have little in common.

Two have more or less semi-cylindrical leaves and are found in Spain, namely *C. carpetanus* and *C. nevadensis*.

C. Fleischeri and *C. parviflorus* are alike in their tunics, which differ from those of any other species in the silky interwoven fibres which resemble those of *Iris (Gynandriris) Sisyrinchium* more than that of a Crocus.

Besides these I have included a few either imperfectly described or not in cultivation.

C. carpetanus of Boissier and Reuter occurs only at high altitudes in a limited area in Spain and in Portugal. It is abundant in the Sierra de Guadarrama in Spain, and on the Sierra d'Estrella and near Coimbra in Portugal. It has never been widely cultivated and I regret that it has died out here, after doing well for a few seasons, both in the rock garden and Crocus frame. It is a very distinct and curious species as to its leaves, tunic and pistil.

The tunic is thick and soft like a wad of tow, composed of fine, yellowish, netted strands lengthening out at the summit of the corm into long, silky hairs which form a cap over an inch in length.

The leaf is semi-cylindrical in cross section, having no trace of the usual blades, but appears to be composed of the keel only with numerous parallel ribs running through the whole length, and minute hairs fringing its two outer edges.

The flowers are rather small, with segments no more than an inch in length. In the forms that I have grown they were of a very delicate shade of lilac with grey-blue veining and some were nearly white in the centre of each segment. Maw found white forms, but like the lilac ones they were veined externally with bluish lines.

The pistil is very remarkable, for the short, nearly entire stigmatic branches are of much the same shade of lilac as the segments. The only other species known with a lilac pistil is *C. byzantinus* (*C. iridiflorus*), which is totally different in its distribution and all its principal characters from *C. carpetanus*.

C. nevadensis of Amo and Campo is the same as Pomel's *C. atlanticus* and Baker's *C. algeriensis*. Like *C. Salzmannii* it is found both in Europe and Africa; it occurs in the Sierra Nevada above Granada and on the Sierra de San Cristoval in Spain, and in Algeria near the Moroccan frontier in the province of Oran from Daiza to Garronban. I have only grown the Spanish plant and found it difficult to flower, and lost it after a few years. It throve best in a sandy bed in the rock garden. It is an interesting rather than a beautiful species, for the starry flowers are very pallid, greenish yellow in the throat and finely veined with pale lilac on a pinkish-white ground. They are funnel shaped and seldom open out fully, even in strong sunshine. The leaves are much like those of *C. carpetanus* but have a shallow furrow on either side dividing the keel from the blade.

The appearance of leaf and flower suggests some Romulea rather than a Crocus, and makes one feel that this and the allied *C. carpetanus* stand half-way between those two genera. The stigmata are frilled and white and unlike those of any other species.

C. Fleischeri of J. Gay can never be mistaken either dormant or when flowering. The tunic is a wonderful piece of natural weaving, its fine strands being so closely interwoven that it seems to be platted. This character caused Maw to place it and *C. parviflorus* in a section including only those two species which he designated *Intertexti*. Even should the tunic be wanting, the corm of *C. Fleischeri* is so yellow that it is easily recognised.

It pushes up fine, grassy leaves in January and is one of the earlier spring species to flower. The segments are white, and variously striped with purple on the outer segments, they are very narrow for their length, less than a quarter of an inch wide and well over an inch long. The flower is very graceful in outline and more starry than any other Crocus when open.

The finely divided stigmata are scarlet and very beautiful, and of such a bright colour that they can be seen through the white segments of a closed flower, and remind me of the yolk seen through the shell of a woodpecker's egg. It grows in Asia Minor around Smyrna and in the Cilician Taurus, and although such a seemingly frail plant is remarkably hardy and easily grown.

C. parviflorus of Baker is only known by the specimens gathered by Mrs. Danford near Anascha in the Cilician Taurus, and now in the Kew Herbarium. They resemble *C. Fleischeri* in the interwoven fibres of their corm tunics, but they are clearly distinguishable by their minute lilac flowers and undivided stigmata.

C. alatavicus was described by Regel of Petersburg in 1869. It is found in the Dzungarian Ala Tau and neighbouring tracts of country in western Turkistan, and is the only Crocus known from so far to the north and east in Central Asia. In general appearance it looks like a white form of *C. Korolkowii*, which is the only other species found east of the Caspian Sea. Their leaves alone would be sufficient to distinguish them, however, *C. alatavicus* having a convex ribbed keel and *C. Korolkowii* a concave one. In the latter also the leaves are remarkably more numerous and narrower than in *C. alatavicus*. Both species have diphyllous proper spathes, no basal spathe and entire stigmata, but *C. alatavicus* has a thinner tunic and smaller corms which together with its distinct leaves and white flowers render it specifically distinct from its somewhat similar yellow-flowered neighbour.

Some years ago it promised to be a free flowering and easily grown species, but has almost disappeared from cultivation.

The large pointed flowers are white internally with a yellow throat, and vary a good deal as to the external markings. A form with dull buff exterior from meadows near Alma Ata was named variety *albus* by Regel and *ochroleucus* by Baker. I saw specimens of this in Miss Willmott's garden at Warley Place, but it is not so beautiful as the forms that are freckled or striped with a rich brownish-purple. It flowers in February, and throws up several blossoms in succession from one shoot.

C. Leichtlinii is a curious, greenish-yellow flowered Crocus given specific rank by me in 1924 in the first edition of this handbook.

It was described by D. Dewar as a variety of *C. biflorus* in the *Gardeners' Chronicle*, vol. 9, p. 235 (1891), from specimens collected at Mardin in Asia Minor, and sent by Max Leichtlin to Kew.

Its corm tunic is quite distinct from that of *C. biflorus* as it splits downwards and upwards into pointed strips, and there are no rings of tunic towards the base such as are the chief distinguishing feature of *C. biflorus* and the other annulate species.

The vandyked, incurving lower portion of the tunic is somewhat like that of *C. laevigatus* but is not so hard nor so dark in colour. The tunic of *C. Crewei* as shown in Fitch's drawing in t. 6168 of the *Botanical Magazine* is rather like that of this species from Mardin, as to the upper teeth, but the lower strips are square at their tips as drawn by Fitch, but sharply pointed in *C. Leichtlinii*.

The upper points bend outwards round the base of the sheathing scales, and the lower points curve inwards, fitting the base of the corm and allowing the roots to escape through the slits. There is also an inner tunic of thinner texture split upwards into shorter points than those of the outer tunic, but it only reaches downwards for about a third of the corm and ends in a straight, very slightly split, edge. The basal tunic is very small, a coriaceous disc with a fringed edge. The leaves are narrow, about six in number.

There is no basal spathe and the proper spathes are diphyllous. The flowers are small, the segments an inch long and a third of an inch wide, the three outer yellowish externally with a band of slatey-grey up the centre; the inner segments are paler with a greenish-blue spot at their bases. The throat is orange, unbearded, and the yellow anthers are marked with greenish-grey stripes up the centre of both faces, and are twice as long as the yellow glabrous filaments. The stigmata are scarlet, slightly toothed, and reach only a little way above the bases of the anthers. It flowers early in February and is fragrant, but has a strange faded or washed-out appearance, being of such pale shades of yellow and greyish-lilac, with a curious tint of green throughout.

It has seeded with Mr. Peter Barr, and the seedlings are exactly like the wild collected form. Such a distinct plant deserves specific rank.

C. tauri melanthorus, mentioned by the late Mr. James Allen in the *Gardeners' Chronicle*, vol. *13*, p. 226 (1893) is another imperfectly described plant. It was sent by Whittall from Smyrna, and has the tunic of an annulate species, such as *C. biflorus*, of hard coriaceous substance, not a thin membrane as in *C. tauri* proper.

It bears very small, remarkably globose lilac flowers in February. The outer segments, less than an inch in length, have a dark reddish-purple band up their centres externally. The orange in the throat shows through to the outside where the base of the segments is almost red, but not so bright as in Moon's drawing in which it is No. 1 on the plate facing page 104 of *Flora and Sylva*, vol. 2 (1904). The stigmata are scarlet, entire and longer than the deep black, curiously hastate anthers.

It is an attractive species, although so small in all its parts, as the black anthers and scarlet stigmata give the flower a peculiar charm. It increases slowly by division and has not yet borne seeds, so that it is still a very scarce plant.

A few other imperfectly known species deserve mention:

C. lazicus of Boissier, discovered by Balansa in 1866 in moist meadows above Djimel, south-east of Trebizond, in Lazistan, is only known from the dried specimens then gathered. It is uncertain whether it was flowering in June or August and is remarkable for the very curious characteristic that the sheathing scales are shorter than the basal spathe. It bears a fine yellow flower and increases by underground stolons after the manner of *C. nudiflorus* and *C. gargaricus*, and would be a very desirable addition to cultivated species.

C. Biliottii of Maw, *Mon. Croc.*, Plate *56b*, also grows near Trebizond and was found near Stauros flowering in May. Maw cultivated it, but it was lost until collected again by E. K. Balls.

It has much the appearance of *C. aërius* but differs in the tunic, which splits downwards into loose fibres and is without rings at the base.

C. montenegrinus of Kerner was found by Herr Maly on Mount Orgen, in Montenegro. The specimens he dried have very peculiar stigmatic growths attached to the tips of the anthers, which look like an abnormal outgrowth, but as Kerner at first labelled the specimens as *C. appendiculatus* and afterwards changed the name, it looks as though all those gathered were alike. Maw's Plate *23* in his monograph shows the throat as yellow and the stigma as divided at the level of the throat into long, narrow entire branches. But for these three characters it closely approaches *C. vernus*. The late Oskar Bierbach collected some corms for me from the locality where *C. montenegrinus* was found, but they are a small form of *C. vernus*, with white or lilac-veined flowers, very much like the variety *siculus*.

C. mouradi from Mourad-dagh, Smyrna, is described in *The Garden*, vol. *35*, p. 473 (1889), as being intermediate between *C. chrysanthus* and *C. aureus*, with bright orange flowers and pale yellow anthers and stigmata. I have not seen specimens.

C. Jessoppiae is a name attached provisionally in 1924 to a remarkable though small species that appeared among some seedlings and off-sets I gave to my neighbour the late Miss Euphemia Jessopp.

The flowers are somewhat similar to those of *C. Pestalozzae*, but are larger with stronger blue markings at the base of the outer segments.

Its most distinct character is the curiously coarse parallel fibres of the corm tunic, which are like those of *C. candidus*, but its narrow leaves and undivided stigmata distinguish it from that species. I think it must be a hybrid and that its parents were some white form of *C. chrysanthus*, and either *C. candidus* or some species with a strongly netted corm tunic.

It flowers remarkably freely early in March and has increased well, but has produced no seed.

XIII

Notes on the Bibliography of the Crocus

A LONG annotated list of books and papers dealing with the
Crocus is given in George Maw's *Monograph of the Genus Crocus*,
but only the more important and interesting among them are
mentioned below, arranged according to their dates of
publication.

1542. FUCHS, LEONHART. *De Historia Stirpium*. Basel.

The only Crocus figured in Fuchs's great herbal is *Crocus
sativus*. The plate on page 441 (t. ccxlviii of the 1543 German
edition, *New Kreuterbuch*) represents two plants, one in flower,
the other in leaf. It falls below the general accuracy shown by
the skilful artist Heinrich Fullmaurer, since one of the two
flowers is drawn with only four perianth segments and the
leaves normally present at flowering time scarcely protrude
beyond the sheath.

1576. CLUSIUS, CAROLUS (CHARLES DE L'ECLUSE). *Rariorum
aliquot Stirpium per Hispanias observatarum Historia*. Antwerp.

In this pioneer flora of Spain and Portugal Clusius described
and illustrated with woodcuts (later reproduced and copied in
many other books) the new plants discovered on his journey
there in 1564 and 1565 as tutor to the sons of Anton Fugger.
These included two Romuleas (*Romulea Clusiana* and *Romulea
uliginosa*, figured as *Crocus vernus minor*) and a Crocus under the
name *Crocum montanum* which appears to be *C. asturicus* but is
presumably *C. Clusii*. He also gave a figure of *Crocus vernus* from
Italy and the Alps.

1578. DODOENS, REMBERT. *A nievve Herball* first translated
out of French by Henry Lyte. London.

This English translation of Dodoens, *Histoire des Plantes*
(1557), which was a French translation by Clusius of his
Cruydeboeck, gives a copy (reversed and much reduced) of the
illustrations of *Crocus sativus* in Fuchs's *De Historia Stirpium*.

1581. L'Obel, Matthias de (M. Lobelius). *Plantarum seu Stirpium Icones*. Antwerp.

Ten woodcuts appear in this work under the name of Crocus, but three of them represent species of Romulea discovered by Clusius (pages 141, 142), whose illustrations are here reprinted. *Crocus sativus* is portrayed on page 137 in flower and full leaf. Clusius's *Crocum montanum* is here called *Crocus montanus autumnalis*. The other woodcuts appear to represent white and violet forms of *C. vernus*. The text relating to these was published in L'Obel's *Plantarum seu Stirpium Historia* (1576).

1590. Tabernaemontanus, Jacobus Theodorus. *Eicones Plantarum*. Frankfurt am Main.

Two woodcuts on pages 633 and 634 in this work portray *Crocus sativus*; one shows flowers and leaves, the other leaves only. The two other plants figured as Crocuses are Romuleas.

1597. Gerard, John. *The Herball or Generall Historie of Plantes*. London.

Gerard used the same wood-blocks as Tabernaemontanus of *Crocus sativus* but fell into error when he described the flower as rising 'out of the ground nakedly.' In his chapter on 'Wild Saffron' he likewise figured Romuleas as Crocuses. The text under these refers, however, to what would seem to be purple and white varieties of *C. vernus*, an autumn-flowering species, probably *C. nudiflorus*, 'destitute of those chives which yield the colour, smell or taste that right manured saffron hath,' and a spring-flowering species 'with flowers of a most perfect shining yellow colour, seeming a far off to be a hot glowing cole of fire,' which must be *C. aureus*.

1601. Clusius, Carolus (Charles de l'Ecluse). *Rariorum Plantarum Historia*. Antwerp.

Twelve woodcuts, afterwards used by Johnson and other writers, appear under the heading *Crocum vernum* and *C. montanum* (pages 203-9) in this work. Most of them represent forms of *C. vernus*, one on page 205 is *C. aureus* and two on page 206 *C. susianus*. The second of these shows a semi-double variety, and has been often copied to illustrate other books, e.g. Passe's *Hortus Floridus*. The figures on pages 207-8 represent Romuleas, i.e. *Romulea Clusiana*, *R. uliginosa*, *R. gaditana*.

Clusius's *Crocum montanum* was first published in his *Rariorum aliquot Stirpium per Hispanias*, 265 (1576).

1614. PASSE, CRISPIAN DE (CRISPIJN VANDE PAS), THE YOUNGER.
   Hortus floridus, Autumnus, Hyemalis. Utrecht.

This contains some of the most beautiful engravings of flowers ever produced. Those of *Crocus sativus* (Aut., t. 23), *C. nudiflorus* (Aut., t. 24), and *C. vernus* (Hyem., t. 7) are very good portraits. Equally realistic is the portrait of a little mouse nibbling a Crocus corm!

1629. PARKINSON, JOHN. *Paradisi in Sole Paradisus terrestris.* London.

Parkinson wrote of twenty-seven forms of Crocus as though they were then cultivated in England.

1670. HERTODT A TODENFELD, JOHANN FERDINAND. *Crocologia, seu curiosa Croci, regis vegetabilium, enucleatio.* Jena.

This curious little book deals mostly with the medicinal uses of Saffron, but describes twenty forms of Crocus, many of which can be recognised. For further information see Chapter VI (p. 64).

1753. LINNAEUS, CAROLUS (CARL VON LINNÉ). *Species Plantarum.* Stockholm.

The starting-point of modern botanical nomenclature for Crocus as for other genera. It is worth noting that Linnæus could have had but little knowledge of living Crocuses. Thus he classed the Saffron Crocus as the variety *officinalis* and all the vernal Crocuses as the variety *vernus* of his species *C. sativus*.

1768. MILLER, PHILIP. *The Gardeners' Dictionary.* 8th ed. London.

The eighth edition of this work is the last published in Miller's lifetime and the first in which the Linnæan binomial system of nomenclature was adopted. Miller enumerated twelve varieties of spring and four of autumn Crocuses. The name *C. biflorus* was first published here. The account of the cultivation of Saffron is of great interest.

1770. WESTON, RICHARD. *Botanicus universalis et Hortulanus . . . . The Universal Botanist and Nurseryman.* London.

Here, in vol. 2, 237-40, are listed with brief Latin

descriptions fifty kinds of Crocus previously enumerated by Tournefort. For notes on this book see pages 146-47.

1809. HAWORTH, ADRIAN HARDY. On the Cultivation of
    Crocuses, with a short Account of the different Species
    known at present. *Trans. Hort. Soc. London*, *1*, 122-39.

This paper describes thirteen forms and is accompanied by a good coloured figure of *Crocus stellaris*. Haworth divided his species into *Vernales* flowering in spring and *Autumnales* flowering in autumn, the *Vernales* he further subdivided into *Piligeri* with bearded throats and *Depilati* with hairless throats.

1817. GOLDBACH, KARL LUDWIG. Monographiae Generis Croci
    Tentamen. *Mém. Soc. Imp. Nat. Moscou*, *5*, 142-61.

The first attempt at a monograph of the genus Crocus as a whole.

1826. TENORE, MICHELE. *Memoria sulle Specie e Varietà de Crochi
    della Flora Napolitana*. Naples.

In this memoir Tenore described and figured four Italian species, including *C. Imperati*, which still stands under the name given by him. He also described these in his *Flora Napolitana* of 1836.

1827-32. GAY, JACQUES.

In a detailed and critical review (published in July 1827 in Férrusac, *Bull. Sci. Nat.*, *11*, 346-72) of the memoirs by Bertoloni and Tenore on the Italian species of Crocus, Jacques Gay stated that for ten years he had been assembling material for a monograph of the genus Crocus. Later, in January 1832 (in Férrusac, *Bull. Sci. Nat.*, *25*, 319-21), he published short Latin descriptions of eight new species (*CC. Olivieri, Fleischeri, Adami, Sieberi, Boryi, Tournefortii, banaticus, Clusii, Salzmanni, Cambessedesii* and *insularis*), but the monograph itself never appeared. For this work Gay had some very beautiful drawings made by various French artists, which are now in the Herbarium library of the Royal Botanic Gardens, Kew. They are worthy of study by all who can appreciate the beauty of drawings or of a Crocus. Gay's herbarium is incorporated in the Kew Herbarium, but unfortunately the Gay manuscripts at Kew do not include his unpublished monograph.

1827. KER, JOHN BELLENDEN (earlier GAWLER). *Iridearum Genera.* Bruxelles.

This work contains descriptions of fifteen Crocuses and is useful in bringing together references to literature by earlier authors. Ker, whose original name was Gawler, described many of the Crocuses figured in the early numbers of the *Botanical Magazine*.

1829-30. SABINE, JOSEPH. An Account and Description of the Species and most remarkable Varieties of Spring Crocuses, cultivated in the Garden of the Horticultural Society. *Trans. Hort. Soc. London,* 7, 419-32 (1829), 433-98 (1830).

A well-coloured plate accompanying the text shows nineteen varieties and a great number of others grown in the Society's garden at Chiswick are described.

1841-7. WILLIAM HERBERT, Dean of Manchester.

This skilled botanist and keen gardener commenced his 'Crocorum Synopsis' in the *Botanical Magazine*, 67, under t. 3861 (April 1841), which was continued under tt. 3862-8, 3870-1, 3873-5 (June 1841). He contributed many drawings and descriptions to later volumes and also to the *Botanical Register* until his death in 1846. His most important work, 'A History of the Species of Crocus,' was published in *Journal Hort. Soc. London,* 2, 249-93 (1847). The manuscript, almost finished by the Dean a few days before his death, was placed at the disposal of the Society by his executors. It is a masterly work and the foundation of all later classifications of the genus. The author travelled in eastern Europe and collected plants himself, and was wonderfully successful in obtaining so many new forms, considering the difficulties of transport in his day. The Lindley Library, Royal Horticultural Society, London, possesses a volume of original drawings by Herbert of Crocuses and other bulbous plants.

1873. In this year JOHN GILBERT BAKER published his 'Review of the known Species of Crocus' in the *Gardeners' Chronicle, 1873*, 107-8, etc. (Jan. 1873, etc.). In its final form it is included in that author's *Handbook of the Irideae*, published in 1892.

Sixty-six species are described, and the great value of the

work lies in its concise form and citation of figures. The classification is based on the extent of division of the style-branches, which too frequently brings together species differing widely in other characters.

1876. MAW, GEORGE. 'On Vernal Croci.' *Gardeners' Chronicle, 1876*, 536.

This short note on *Crocus biflorus* and other species is of interest as the first of the many publications on Crocus by George Maw and shows that, although his monograph did not appear until 1886, he had already studied the specimens of Tenore and Gussone at Naples.

1886. MAW, GEORGE. *A Monograph of the Genus Crocus, with an Appendix on the Etymology of the Words Crocus and Saffron by C. C. Lacaita.* London.

George Maw (1832-1912) spent over eight years in preparing this comprehensive and magnificent work. It is one of the finest monographs ever produced, both as regards the accuracy of the information and the beautiful coloured plates it contains. Were it but up to date as to recently collected and garden-raised forms, and less costly, there would be no need for this handbook. I gladly take this opportunity of stating that most of my knowledge of the Crocus family and much of my enjoyment in its cultivation are due to the labours of George Maw as recorded in the pages of his book.

Maw's Crocus herbarium is at the Department of Botany, British Museum (Natural History), London, his Crocus drawings at the Herbarium, Royal Botanic Gardens, Kew. He was a brilliant, many-sided man, distinguished as chemist, geologist and traveller as well as botanist and gardener.

1935. KOMAROV, VLADIMIR L. *Flora URSS*, *4*, 499-511. Leningrad.

The account by Boris Fedtschenko of the species of Crocus occurring within the Soviet Union describes 19, among them the little-known Caucasian *CC. artvinensis, karsianus* and *Roopiae* and a new species, *C. Michelsonii*, from the Kopet Dagh, Turkmen.

XIV

Crocus vernus, the Name and Its History

By B. L. Burtt

THE scope of this study is the early history of three spring-flowering Crocuses to which the name *Crocus vernus* has been applied. In the standard work on the genus, the sumptuous monograph by G. Maw published in 1886, these species appear under the names *C. vernus* Allioni (the early purple Crocus), *C. susianus* Ker-Gawler (the Cloth of Gold Crocus) and *C. aureus* Smith (the early yellow Crocus), but it will be shown that a revision of this nomenclature is unavoidable. The history of Crocuses prior to the publication of Linnæus's *Species Plantarum* in 1753 (the accepted date for the beginning of botanical nomenclature) is very considerable, but its complete investigation, which is so desirable, would be a very laborious piece of work and is not at the moment a practical possibility, even with respect to these three species. The present paper therefore deals with the pre-Linnæan literature only in so far as it actually affects the modern classification and nomenclature of the species under consideration.

Tournefort, in his *Institutiones Rei Herbariae* (1700), a synopsis of all the plants then known, enumerated forty-six different kinds of Crocus, but many of them were only garden varieties, products of more than a century of enthusiastic culture, and they have no claim to specific rank. It seems probable, however, that some fifteen species of the seventy-five or so that are accepted to-day, had already been discovered at that time.

Linnæus included all the true Crocuses known to Tournefort under one species, *Crocus sativus* L., with all the spring-flowering kinds as a variety, *β. vernus* L. This failure to recognise any specific distinctions within the genus *Crocus*, as limited to-day,* was a very drastic reaction from the immoderate multiplication

* *Crocus Bulbocodium* L. is *Romulea Bulbocodium* (L.) Seb. & Mauri.

of names which had taken place in the previous two hundred years, and resulted in the temporary submergence of several good species.

After Linnæus the first step back towards the recognition of the various species of *Crocus* was taken by John Hill in his large work *The Vegetable System*. He dealt with the genus *Crocus* in vol. X, and recognised two species, *C. vernus* and *C. sativus*. Under the latter he describes the cultivated Saffron Crocus, and says: 'This has been thought only a variety of the former, but it is a distinct species.' This is undoubtedly a reference to the work of Linnæus, for no other author had adopted that standpoint. The precise citation for the name of the Saffron is therefore *Crocus sativus* L. emend. Hill.

Hill's *C. vernus* is still a mixed species, the characters he gives being those which distinguish the spring Crocuses from the autumnal Saffron. He says:

'The Leaves are grassy with some breadth; the Style is hid within the flower.

'This is a perennial, native of Switzerland; the common spring crocus of our gardens. It flowers in March. The leaves are of a fine green with a pale rib; the flowers are of a bright yellow, or of a fine purple.'

Crocus vernus Hill is the earliest and only legitimate use of this much overworked name, but to be of any value in modern taxonomy it must be given a precise application; this has not hitherto been done.* In deciding how to apply the name we have only Hill's written word to go on, for his figure is quite unrecognisable as any particular species of *Crocus* and can be left out of account. The first point to notice is that, whereas

* Mansfeld's view (see Fedde, Rep. Sp. Nov. XLIX, 44 : 1940) that Miller's use of *C. vernus* for a yellow species constitutes an emendation of *C. vernus* Hill is quite untenable. In the first place the identification of *C. vernus* Mill. with *C. aureus* Sm. (i.e. the common yellow crocus of gardens) is quite erroneous, for Miller's description is clearly in every particular *C. susianus* Ker-Gawl. (see below, p. 144), which is a distinct species not included in *C. vernus* Hill. Secondly Miller makes no reference whatever to Hill's work, and there is nothing to show that he was adopting his name : Miller's treatment can therefore scarcely be taken as an emendation of Hill's ideas.

Linnæus's *C. sativus* var. *vernus* included all the spring Crocuses known up to that time, Hill's species refers only to the 'common spring crocus of our gardens' with flowers 'of a bright yellow, or of a fine purple.' This clearly restricts his use of the name to cover the two common species which Maw called *C. vernus* All. (purple) and *C. aureus* Sm. (yellow). Of these two only the former is found in Switzerland, which Hill gives as the native country of *C. vernus*; *C. aureus* is not found west of modern Yugoslavia in the wild state.

It is therefore considered that the restriction of *C. vernus* Hill to the purple species (that is to *C. vernus* All. in Maw's sense) is justified. But this is still a composite species; can we give a more precise typification of it? I think not. The form of *C. vernus* found in the Swiss Alps is either white, violet or striped; spring Crocuses 'of a fine purple' come from farther south in Italy. The following conclusion has been reached: the name *C. vernus* Hill emend. is the correct name for the group called *C. vernus* Allioni by Maw. If this is split into smaller species these component units must be designated by names capable of more precise definition.

The next important treatment of the genus after Hill is that of Philip Miller in the eighth edition of his famous *Gardeners' Dictionary* (1768). But whereas in the sixth edition (1752) he had recorded twenty-three different kinds under their pre-Linnæan multiverbal names, in the seventh edition, where his concept of a species approximated closely to the Linnæan, he had only four main species, and in the eighth edition, in which he adopted biverbal nomenclature, only these four were named. They were:

C. sativus L.—the Saffron Crocus.
C. autumnalis Mill.—a doubtful species.
C. vernus Mill.
C. biflorus Mill.—the well-known vernal species with annulate corm.

Of these we are now concerned only with the third, and it must be made clear that this is an entirely independent use of the name *C. vernus* for a species; Miller makes no reference at all to Hill's work, and *C. vernus* Mill. is a later homonym of

C. vernus Hill, and must be rejected. It is, however, of great interest to investigate the identity of this plant and his account is therefore quoted in full:

'3. *Crocus* (*Vernus*) spatha bivalvi radicali, floribus sessilibus. Crocus with a bivalve spatha near the root and flowers sitting close to the ground. *Crocus vernus latifolius, flavo flore, varius* C.B.P. 66. Commonly called Bishop's Crocus.

.   .   .   .   .

'The third sort hath a pretty large compressed bulbous root, *covered with a light brown netted skin*, from which arise four or five leaves, like those of the other vernal Crocuses, of a purplish colour on their lower parts; from between these come out one or two *flowers of a deep yellow colour*, sitting close between the young leaves *never rising above two inches high*; these have an agreeable odour; *the outer segments of the petal are marked with three black streaks or stripes running lengthways from the bottom to the top of the segment*; these are narrower than the inner segments. From the double arrangement of these segments some have called it a double flower. *These segments have dark purple bottoms, and the tube of the flower hath as many purple stripes as there are segments in the petal.* Out of the centre of the tube arises a slender style, crowned by a golden stigma, which is broad and flat, and is attended by three slender stamina of the same length, terminated by yellow summits. After the flower has passed, the germen pushes out of the ground and swells to a roundish three-cornered seed-vessel, which opens in three parts and is filled with roundish brown seeds. This is one of the earliest Crocuses in spring.'

In reproducing this description I have italicised certain characters which those who are familiar with garden Crocuses will recognise as being indisputable characteristics of the species currently known as *Crocus susianus* Ker-Gawl. (*Bot. Mag.*, t. 652: 1803). If further proof of this were required it is given by the fact that the synonym cited for *C. vernus* by Miller, namely *Crocus vernus latifolius flavoflore varius* of Caspar Bauhin (*Pinax*, 66: 1623), was also cited by Ker-Gawler for his

C. susianus. I shall return to the question of the correct name for this species later, and its pre-Linnæan history can then also be examined in greater detail; meanwhile further uses of the name *C. vernus* must engage our attention.

Crocus vernus Allioni first appears in that author's little-known *Auctarium ad Synopsim methodicam Stirpium Horti Regii Taurinensis* (1772-3),* but only as a bare name without description, and its valid publication by Allioni had to await the appearance of his *Flora Pedemontana* (I, p. 84) in 1785. In this latter work Allioni quoted as a synonym *C. tuba brevissima trifida* of Haller (*Hist. Stirp. Helv.*, II, p. 127, No. 1257), which is, as regards the description, the small purple or white vernal Crocus of the Swiss and Italian Alps, the Cevennes and the Tyrol, and this is doubtless the plant intended by Allioni as *C. vernus.*

Between the dates of these two publications, however, the name *Crocus vernus* had independently been given specific rank by Wulfen (in Jacquin, *Fl. Austr.*, V, 47 app., t.36: 1778). Both the description given by Wulfen and the coloured illustration refer to the same plant as Allioni's *C. vernus*, but it is clear from the remarks and synonymy that Wulfen had no intention of restricting the name to any particular form, but used it to embrace all the spring-flowering Crocuses, yellow or mauve. It is, in fact, correct to cite this as *C. vernus* (L.) Wulfen (= *C. sativus* L. β. *vernus* L.). Both this and *C. vernus* All. are independent later homonyms of *C. vernus* Hill, of which they are also, in greater part, synonyms.

C. vernus was accepted in Wulfen's sense by Curtis, who illustrated a yellow Crocus under this name (*Bot. Mag.*, t. 45, 1787). The plant figured by Curtis doubtless fell within the limits accorded by Lamarck to his *Crocus luteus* (*Tabl. Encycl.*, I, 106: 1791), which he distinguished from the purple species referred to as '*C. vernus* L.' Lamarck believed *C. luteus* to be a

* The precise date of this work has never, to my knowledge, been settled. There is, however, in Linnæus's correspondence at the Linnean Society of London a letter from Allioni written on 15th February, 1772, in which he says " Paro nunc quamprimum Auctarium. . . ." The copy sent to Linnæus was a reprint with separate pagination : the work originally formed part of Volume V of *Mélange de Philosophie et de Mathématique* of the Société Royale de Turin.

native of the Swiss Alps, but this is a clear error, for no wild yellow Crocus grows west of the Balkans. Later Ker-Gawler, ignoring Lamarck, made Curtis's illustration of *C. vernus* the basis of his *C. maesiacus* (*Bot. Mag.*, sub t. 652: 1803). It may be mentioned, however, that Curtis's plant is not the true *Crocus vernus maesiacus* of Clusius, which was described shortly afterwards by Smith as *C. aureus* (*Fl. Graec. Prodr.*, 24: 1806).

Of the names mentioned so far *C. vernus* Hill, *C. vernus* Mill. and *C. luteus* Lam. have been strangely disregarded by subsequent authors, but the remainder are well known. We must now turn to a work which has been almost entirely ignored by more recent writers—*The Universal Botanist* of Richard Weston, a work in four octavo volumes of which the second, which includes the account of *Crocus*, appeared in 1771. Since it will be shown in what follows that some of the *Crocus* names proposed by Weston must now be accorded overdue recognition as the earliest names for the species concerned, it may be desirable to give some brief information about the work. Weston set out to make the Linnæan system of classification available to the English horticulturist. As the first volume of the *Universal Botanist* appeared in 1770 it may well be that its preparation was under way before the eighth edition of Philip Miller's *Gardener's Dictionary* was published. Weston makes no reference to Miller's weighty tome,* nor to Hill's *Vegetable System* in twenty-six volumes, but he remarks (Introduction, p. x) '. . . the student, however tenacious may be his memory, finds it extremely difficult to carry with him the descriptions and nice distinctions of so vast a multiplicity of plants from the closet into the garden, forest or field. Voluminous publications are therefore more improperly calculated for the cultivation of the Science of Botany than that of any other,' and such words, unless entirely innocent, can scarcely have been aimed elsewhere. In applying the Linnæan nomenclature to cultivated plants Weston found that a few of those he regarded as distinct species had not been so recognised by Linnæus. He therefore created new biverbal names for them, linking these with a diagnostic phrase which is usually taken word for word from

* It tips the scales at 14 lb. and measures $16\frac{3}{4}$ in. × 10 in. × $3\frac{1}{4}$ in. thick!

the multiverbal name of Tournefort. In so far as Weston's species can now be identified it is by reference to Tournefort's work and the synonyms cited therein; that these are not enumerated at length by Weston himself must be attributed to the exigencies of space in a work of this nature. It is indeed clear that Weston was well acquainted with the botanical literature of his time, both from references in his introduction and from the tables which form part of vol. IV. Here we find that the chronological table of botanical authors which was compiled by Adanson is reprinted, but there is also an original enumeration of botanical literature which is taken right up to 1770 and is a very useful compilation.

Weston dealt with no less than fifty sorts of Crocus, arranging them under thirteen species and their varieties. To what extent his identifications of currently cultivated plants with Tournefort's names can be relied upon is not known, for he left no specimens; however, Weston's biverbal names are validly published as based on the Tournefortian (and occa- sionally other) synonyms and must be considered; the vernal species are:

* 1. *C. vernus* Weston—a later homonym of *C. vernus* Hill.
  2. *C. caeruleus* Weston.
† 3. *C. cinericius* Weston.
* 4. *C. duplex* Weston—refers to a double flowered-form and the name can therefore be rejected.
  5. *C. flavus* Weston.
† 6. *C. janthinus* Weston.
† 7. *C. polyanthus* Weston—this name invalidates the later *C. polyanthus* Grossheim.
  8. *C. purpureus* Weston.
† 9. *C. rubens* Weston.
† 10. *C. violaceus* Weston.
  11. *C. angustifolius* Weston.

The names marked * can be rejected for the reason given. Those marked † are at present doubtful; some of them at least are but garden varieties. The remaining species are, however, of great importance and must be dealt with in detail.

C. caeruleus Weston and *C. purpureus* Weston both fall within the very broad species *C. vernus* Hill as understood above. *C. purpureus* is *C. vernus latifolius flore purpureo magno* of Tournefort (*Inst. Rei Herb.*, 351: 1719), and of C. Bauhin (*Pinax*, 65: 1623), and through these *C. vernus latifolius purpureus flore majore* of Clusius (*Hist. Pl.*, 204; 1601), a Crocus of which Clusius received corms from Naples in 1592 and which flowered later at Leyden. The description, and the known origin from Naples, leave no doubt that Clusius had the large purple Crocus of southern Italy which was subsequently named *C. vernus* var. *neapolitanus* Ker-Gawl. (*Bot. Mag.*, t. 860: 1805). For this, then, we may adopt the specific name *C. purpureus* Weston if *C. vernus* Hill is subdivided.

C. caeruleus is the *C. vernus latifolius flore violaceo vel caeruleo distincto* of Tournefort (*Inst. Rei Herb.*, 351: 1819) and C. Bauhin (*Pinax*, 66, 1623). This unites two earlier names; one is the *C. violaceus et caeruleus distinctus* of Sweert's *Florilegium* (1612), and is not now identifiable, the other *C. vernus latifolius flore violaceo* of Besler's *Hortus Eystettensis* (*Vern.*, II, fol. 3, no. 3). It is scarcely possible to say with certainty precisely which form of the purple spring-flowering Crocus served for illustration, but it is worth noting that the preceding species was *C. vernus flore candido* and the figures show no differences between these two. The synonymy quoted by Besler leads, as we shall show, to a Crocus which is well known to occur in purple-flowered and white-flowered forms. The main synonyms are 'Dodoens 214' (Dodoens, *Stirpium Historiae Pemptades sex*, 214: 1583) and 'Lobel, obser. 68' (Lobel, *Plantarum seu stirpium historia, stirpium observationes*, 68: 1576), and they have one element in common. We find in both places, as so often happens among these early herbals, that the same illustration is reproduced. In Dodoens it is entitled *Crocus silvestris vernalis prior* and the information about it is very scanty; in Lobel it is called *C. sylvestris vernus tertius, flore albo purpuroviolacea basi advers. p. 53*, and in a marginal note is the additional information 'Albo colore variat pediculo caeruleo alias albo in Ostensi valle ad radices praecessi Bernardi montis.' This is invaluable, for it shows at once that Lobel was describing a truly wild plant and not one of the many Crocus forms which were known only in gardens. Turning to the

Stirpium adversaria nova of Lobel and Pena (53: 1571), we find a description, under the heading *Crocus sylvestris montanus flore albo*, of which the following is a free translation:

> 'The flower of *sylvestris*, however, comes only rarely in autumn, but generally in early spring; it is smaller, white, sometimes purple, especially in chilly places where the snow lies; thus there are in the bleak valleys of Aosta, not far from Mt. St. Bernard, stretches white with winter snow and purple and white with the flowers of this Crocus. The root and stem are similar to *sativus*, the leaf shorter and broader.'

This small purple or white spring-flowering Crocus of Piedmont is thus the basis of *C. caeruleus* Weston.

We have, therefore, these two valid specific names, *C. caeruleus* Weston and *C. purpureus* Weston, for two very different forms included under the broad species *C. vernus* Hill. The question arises whether or not there are two distinct species here. The final solution of this problem will require a far more detailed study of the various geographical forms and their distribution than has yet been made. The present answer must be based on probability and (though *C. vernus* Hill will remain a convenient name for the mixed garden forms), I consider that *C. caeruleus* and *C. purpureus* are best tentatively retained as distinct species. This course is followed, using the names *C. albiflorus* Kit. ex Schultes and *C. vernus* Wulfen, by F. Buxbaum (in Kirchner, Loew and Schröter, *Lebengeschichte Blütenpflanzen Mitteleuropas*, *I. Abt.*, 3872: 1932-3). In general the former seems to be spread across the zone of the south of France, the Swiss, Italian and Austrian Alps and the north-western part of the Balkan Peninsula. *C. purpureus*, on the other hand, is a species of central and southern Italy and of the more central regions of the Balkan Peninsula. The extreme southern *C. siculus* Tineo is also probably a distinct species.

Turning to the yellow-flowered species we find that *C. flavus* Weston is based on *C. vernus latifolius flavus flore majore* Tournefort (*Inst. Rei Herb.*, 352: 1719), which in turn is *C. vernus latifolius flavus* C. Bauhin (*Pinax*, 66: 1623), and hence *C. vernus latifolius flavo flore* of Clusius (*Rar. Stirp. Pannon*, 226: 1583, and *Hist. pl.*, II,

205: 1601). Clusius records the origin of his plant; it was found in Serbia, near Belgrade, in March 1579. As Clusius mentions, the old name for Serbia was Maesia, and in the earlier publication the chapter heading was *De croco verno maesiaco*. It was this epithet *maesiacus* which Ker-Gawler revived and applied to the yellow vernal Crocus of Curtis's *Botanical Magazine* (t. 45), though this was scarcely the same as that described by Clusius (see pp. 98, 146 above).

C. *flavus* Weston is the oldest name for one of the yellow-flowered spring Crocuses and must be typified by this plant described by Clusius; it is well known to botanists to-day, generally under the name *C. aureus* Sm. *C. luteus* Lam. as originally published (*Tabl. Encycl.*, I, 106: 1791) had a very brief unrecognisable description and no synonymy. Later Poiret (in Lam. *Encycl. Méth.*, VI, 385: 1804) added the Tournefort, Bauhin and Clusius synonyms on which *C. flavus* Weston is based, and it seems best to regard *C. luteus* Lam. as a synonym of it.

Finally *C. angustifolius* Weston must be considered. This is one of the few names not based on Tournefort. Weston's reference here is to *C. vernus angustifolius aureus variegatus* of Besler's *Hortus Eystettensis* (Hyem, t. 1, fig. 3: 1613), of which there is an excellent illustration showing the strongly reticulate corm-tunic and brown-marked flowers of *Crocus vernus* Mill. (= *C. susianus* Ker-Gawl.; see p. 144 above). In fact the *Hortus Eystettensis* figure is quoted by Ker-Gawler under *C. susianus*, and he explicitly mentioned the excellence of the illustration. Besler's *Hortus Eystettensis* is an account of the plants in the garden of the Prince Bishop of Eichstätt, and it is quite possible that knowledge of this illustration (though he did not quote it) led Miller to give his *C. vernus* the English name Bishop's Crocus. It is, however, far better known by Parkinson's name, the Cloth of Gold Crocus (*Crocus vernus luteus versicolor primus* Parkinson, *Paradisus Terrestris*, 166, no. 24, t. 163, fig. 11: 1629). It has been in cultivation for more than three hundred years and was known to Clusius (*Hist. Pl.*, II, 206: 1601) as *C. vernus latifolius flavo-vario flore*. *C. angustifolius* Weston is its correct name.

These investigations have thus shown that the following

amendments to the nomenclature of Maw's monograph are needed:

Name in Maw's Monograph	*Name to be adopted*
C. *vernus* Allioni	C. *vernus* Hill,
	comprising
	C. *caeruleus* Weston
	C. *purpureus* Weston
	C. *siculus* Tineo
C. *aureus* Smith	C. *flavus* Weston
C. *susianus* Ker-Gawler	C. *angustifolius* Weston

Having arrived at the earliest valid names for these species, their history will not now be pursued further. The following summary of the nomenclature, which includes some of the more important later references, may be given:

1. CROCUS VERNUS Hill, Veg. Syst., x, 1 (1765), hic emendata. C. *sativus* L.β. *vernus* L.Sp.Pl., I, 36 (1753), pro parte. C. *vernus* (L.) Wulfen in Jacq. Fl. Austr., V, app. 47, t. 36 (1778), pro max. parte. C. *vernus* All. Fl. Pedemont, I, 84 (1785), sec. Maw, Mon. Genus Crocus, 151 (1886).

This is an aggregate species covering the three following microspecies:

1a. C. CAERULEUS Weston, Univ. Bot., II, 237 (1771). C. *sylvestris montanus flore albo* Pena & Lobel, Stirp. Advers. Nov., 53 (1571). C. *sylvestris vernus tertius, flore albo purpuroviolacea basi* Lobel, Pl. Stirp. Hist., Obs. 70 [err. typ. 68] (1576). C. *vernus latifolius flore violaceo vel caeruleo distincto* C. Bauhin, Pinax, 66 (1623); Tournef. Inst. Rei Herb., 351 (1719). C. *tuba brevissima trifida* Haller, Hist. Stirp. Helv., II, 127 (1768). C. *vernus* All. Fl. Pedemont, I, 84 (1785). C. *albiflorus* Kit. ex Schultes, Österr. Fl., ed. 2, I, 101 (1814); Schinz and Keller, Fl. Schweiz, ed. 4, I, 152 (1923); F. Buxbaum in Kirchner, Loew & Schröter, Lebensgeschichte der Blütenpflanzen Mitteleuropas, I Abt. 3,872 (1932-3).

1b. C. PURPUREUS Weston, Univ. Bot., II, 238 (1771). C. *vernus latifolius purpureus flore majore* Clusius, Hist. Pl., 204 (1601). C. *vernus latifolius flore purpureo magno* C. Bauhin, Pinax, 65 (1623); Tournef. Inst. Rei Herb., 351 (1719). C. *vernus latifolius purpureus* [sphalm. *perpetuus*] *flore maiore*

J. Bauhin, Hist. Pl., II, 642 (1651). *C. vernus* Wulf. sec.
F. Buxbaum in Kirchner, Loew & Schröter, Lebensgeschichte
der Blütenpflanzen Mitteleuropas, I. Abt. 3, 872 (1932-3).
C. vernus var. *neapolitanus* Ker-Gawl. in Bot. Mag., t. 860 (1805).
C. napolitanus Loiseleur-Deslongchamps in Mordant de Launay,
Herb. Gén. de l'Amateur, II, t. 101 (1817). *C. neapolitanus*
Ascherson; Bergmans, Vaste Planten, 2nd ed., 251 (1939).

1c. C. SICULUS Tineo in Guss. Fl. Sic. Prod. Suppl., I, 7
(1832). *C. vernus* var. *siculus* (Tineo) Maw in Gard. Chron.
N.S. XVI, 368 (1881); Mon. Genus Crocus, 152 (1886).

2. CROCUS FLAVUS Weston, Univ. Bot., II, 237 (1771).
C. vernus latifolius flavo flore Clusius, Rar. Stirp. Pannon., 226
(1583), et Hist. Pl., II, 205 (1601). *C. vernus latifolius flavus*
C. Bauhin, Pinax, 66 (1623). *C. vernus latifolius flavus flore
majore* Tournef. Inst. Rei Herb. 352 (1719). *C. sativus* L. β.
vernus L. Sp. Pl., I, 36 (1753), pro parte. *C. vernus* (L.) Wulfen
in Jacq. Fl. Austr., V, 47 (1778), quoad syn. pro parte. *C. luteus*
Lam. Tab. Encycl., I, 106 (1791); Poiret in Lam. Encycl.
Méth., VI, 385 (1804). *C. maesiacus* Ker-Gawl. in Bot. Mag.,
sub t. 652 (1803), et in General Indexes Bot. Mag. 22 (1805),
pro parte. *C. aureus* Sm. Fl. Graec. Prodr., 24 (1806) et Fl.
Graec., 25, t. 35 (1806); Maw, Mon. Genus Crocus, 271 (1886).
C. lageniflorus Salisb. Parad. Londin. t. 106 (1806). *C. aureus*
var. *luteus* Bergmans, Vaste Planten, 2nd ed., 249 (1939).

3. CROCUS ANGUSTIFOLIUS Weston, Univ. Bot. II, 238
(1771). *C. vernus latifolius flavo-vario flore* Clusius, Hist. Pl. II,
206 (1601). *C. vernus angustifolius aureus variegatus* Besler, Hort.
Eystett. Hyem., t. 1, fig. 3 (1613). *C. vernus latifolius flavoflore varius* Bauhin, Pinax, 66 (1623); Tournef. Inst. Rei Herb.
352 (1719). *C. vernus luteus versicolor primus* Parkinson, Paradisus
Terrestris, 166, t. 163, fig. 11 (1629). *C. vernus* Mill. Gard. Dict.,
ed. 8, no. 3 (1768)—non Hill. *C. susianus* Ker-Gawl. in Bot.
Mag., t. 652 (1803); Maw, Mon. Genus Crocus, 199 (1886).

XV

Colchicums

COLCHICUMS present difficult problems to both gardener and botanist. The greater number of the handsome members of the genus are easily grown, and the chief trouble in a garden arises from the amount of space required in spring and early summer for their coarse leaves. In autumn the rosy lilac, white or tessellated flowers can never be too numerous, come where they may; but in spring it is almost annoying to watch the unfolding of those great leaves. They expand enormously with the April showers, rise up rapidly on tall shoots and are then ready to fall outwards and sprawl over neater-growing plants that we realise too late have been planted too near the Colchicums. They would make a good edging to beds of shrubs or tall herbaceous plants but for their aggravating habit of beginning to fade and collapse in the first warm days of June. It is bad for the plants to clear away the flabby yellowing leaves, and it is only the truly hopeful-hearted gardener who can find any pleasure in watching their decay, by looking forward to the crop of flowers promised by so much ripening foliage.

For the botanist their evil ways are numerous indeed. In most of them the colour of the styles changes gradually from white to purple according to the age of the flower. The skin of the anthers, which may be yellow or purple before splitting, provides a clue to the identity of a few species, but after the pollen has escaped it is hard, especially in dried specimens, to distinguish the original colour of an anther, and this has caused various authors to disagree in their descriptions. The absence of leaves at the flowering time of so many species is another source of trouble, for it is a difficult matter to gather plants from their native homes at two seasons and yet be certain that leaves and flowers come from the same plant.

Any Colchicum flower that has been dried for more than a year is generally of a singularly dull shade of buff, with an occasional flush of lilac at the tips of the segments. The chequered markings of certain species may disappear entirely in some dried specimens, especially in fully matured blossoms. Now and then a species described as without tessellation bears flowers that are chequered at their first opening, and the markings fade away in a day or two.

Botanists may then be forgiven if we find difficulty in recognising living plants from their descriptions, for there can scarcely be a genus of plants that is harder to describe and classify.

I can only attempt to guide my readers among the intricacies of those forms which I have been able to grow.

The genus Colchicum belongs to the Lily family (Liliaceae) and differs from Crocus in three main characters, the position of the ovary, and the number of the stamens and also of the styles. Superficially there is such a general likeness in the flowers of the two that the misleading names of Meadow Saffron and Autumn Crocus have been used for the Colchicum.

In both genera the ovary is hidden below the ground at flowering time, and the flower is raised on a long perianth tube instead of a stalk.

In Liliaceae the ovary is superior, that is to say, *inside* the perianth tube or the perianth segments, and there are six stamens. These characters are found in a Colchicum, contrasting with the three stamens and the ovary *below* the perianth tube of a Crocus.

Also a Colchicum has three distinct styles arising from the top of the ovary. Though in some species they are joined for a little space about half-way up the tube, they end in three simple stigmatic tips. In a Crocus there is only one style, which is divided into three branches near its summit.

The presence of the six stamens is sufficient in itself to distinguish a Colchicum from a Crocus.

It can be seen in the diagram facing page 20 that the stamens are arranged in two ranks. Those with shorter filaments arise from the inner segments, but so much higher up that the anthers are borne at a higher level than those on the longer filaments.

It is only in *CC. alpinum, corsicum* and *neapolitanum* that all six stamens are inserted at the same level at the base of the segments.

The dormant period of a Colchicum is short. The leaves fade after the ripening of the seed in June, and the corm matures soon after. Those that flower in autumn are ready in August to form new roots and push out flowers. Some species can flower satisfactorily at their natural season without being planted or supplied with any moisture. I have seen a gay show of flowering Colchicums in cottage windows in Cornwall provided by corms laid in a row on the ledge of the bay window.

It is very unusual that a plant brings flowers to perfection while without active roots to supply moisture to the expanding cells. *Sauromatum guttatum*, a large Aroid, has been much advertised as capable of flowering in a dry state. The Aroid produces only one inflorescence, but *C. byzantinum* can bear twelve to twenty flowers in a long succession and without active roots. Gathered flowers of many species will last fresh for several days without being placed in water.

As in the case of a Crocus the dry, resting state of a Colchicum is a corm, a solid underground stem, in which nutriment is stored.

In many species, especially in *C. speciosum* or *C. cilicicum*, the corm is very large, four inches or more in length and about two inches in diameter in the widest part. One of these large corms will repay examination and explain the manner of growth.

It is irregular in shape, one side being convex and the other flattened and prolonged downwards to form a curious foot-like projection, which is a characteristic feature of most species of Colchicum. If the tunic is removed the large white corm is seen to have an upper projection, more pointed than the foot, at the top on the flattened side. A central groove runs down longitudinally on this side, widening towards the base just above the foot. The new bud for the coming season is formed in the hollow at the base of this groove. In a fully grown but unripened corm examined in mid-June this growth bud is very small and looks much like the tiny radicle seen between the two halves of a walnut or filbert kernel. It grows with astonishing rapidity as soon as the corm is ripened.

The tunic when young is a white and fleshy membrane but becomes brown and leathery when mature. It is composed of the tubular lower portion of the first and outermost leaf and completely encloses the whole corm.

It is produced upward above the solid corm into a long, tough, hollow tube, called the cap, which reaches to the surface of the soil and provides an open passage, even in stiff clay soil, through which the slender flower buds can push their way without injury.

In a healthy Colchicum tunic there are only two orifices for the exit of its developing organs, one from the upper end of the cap, which is always open, the other at the base and side of the foot, closed at first, but easily pushed away by the force of the roots, all of which grow from a small definite area on the outer side of the base of the new shoot.

When examined at flowering time the tunic should be slit vertically where it covers the new shoot lying in the groove on the flat side of the corm. When the new shoot is exposed it will be seen that it is only connected to the corm by a remarkably small area at the base, so small that it is hard to believe that, before the roots are developed, all the moisture and nutriment required for the rapid growth of the shoot and its flowers must pass from the storage in the corm through this very small point of attachment.

Beginning from the base it will be found that the new shoot consists of the following parts, a short sheath of about one-eighth of an inch long composed of a delicate white membrane, which soon disappears and so is called the ephemeral sheath. From within this arises a long tubular sheath often four to five inches in length, reaching to the surface of the soil through the passage provided by the previous year's cap. This sheath encloses all the blossoms and leaves which in turn emerge from its open end.

The next organ inside this long sheath is the first and outermost leaf, the blade of which, at this stage of growth, is very little developed, but its tubular base plays a very important part in the life of the plant, as it will eventually form the tunic and cap of the next season's corm.

Also in an axillary position at the base of this leaf, the minute dormant bud, which is the embryo to become next season's shoot, is placed on the outer side of the axis away from the old corm.

The tubular base of this first leaf also encloses the axis of growth from which arise the other leaves, and within their axils or on the summit of the axis arise the pedicels and ovaries of the flowers arranged spirally.

The base of the axis is already enlarged into a globular portion which with further growth will form the new corm. On its upper portion, in the axil of the second leaf, there is often a second dormant embryo, which in a vigorous individual can develop into a flowering shoot on the upper part of the side of the new corm, and later will produce an offset that finally separates from the main corm.

If the main axis bears more flowers than leaves the additional flowers are subtended by minute, colourless, triangular bracts. The axis terminates in a very small point above the insertion of the highest blossom. In a mature corm this small point has developed into a flattened prominence at the base of which is a slight pit, which was the summit of the axis and still contains the dark brown withered bases of the previous season's leaves and flowers. The prominence stands on the flat side of a corm, while on the opposite side of the pit there is a furrow a quarter of an inch wide in its upper part and narrowing until the sides meet lower down. It appears that this furrow is the result of the swelling outwards of two portions of the developing corm, and where they meet we may expect to find the secondary dormant bud mentioned above.

Next spring the leaves develop and emerge above the soil, generally in the form of a rosette. As they do so the old corm shrinks and a new corm begins to develop by its side from the flowering axis of autumn. The remaining nutriment stored in the old corm is used in the development of the fruits and young leaves, until the latter are able to assist in gathering the store of food required for the new corm. The lower portion of the axis develops by downward growth to form the foot or spur.

The corm is thus renewed laterally and always on the flattened side, but does not travel annually more than a fraction of an inch, as the withering and disappearance of the old corm provides the needful space to be occupied by the young corm. Therefore an individual Colchicum occupies almost the same position in the soil for many seasons. An offset, on the contrary, formed on the convex surface pushes away in the opposite direction.

The leaves differ greatly in form and size among the species and also as to the time of their appearance. In most autumn-flowering species such as *CC. autumnale, speciosum byzantinum* and *agrippinum* they do not appear before the following spring and are large and broad; in most of the winter or early spring flowering species they are narrowly linear and accompany the flowers. *CC. Kesselringii* and *Szovitzii* have the narrowest and *byzantinum* and *macrophyllum* have the longest, a foot long and six or more inches in width. In most species they are glabrous, in others pubescent or ciliated on the margins.

As the leaves mature in the end of May the large seed capsules are revealed in the cup formed by the bases of the two or three innermost leaves.

The seed vessel is formed of three distinct carpels, free in their upper half but generally united below. When ripe they open at the summit and the round, thick-coated seeds escape.

From the observations of Professor Rolf Nordhagen, recorded in a Norwegian periodical, *Bergens Museums Årbok,* 1933, Naturvid. rekke, No. 2 (1933), it seems probable that the seeds of Colchicum are distributed by ants. He found that those of *C. autumnale* and *C. speciosum* are covered when ripe with a sugary layer which is attractive to ants, and he watched ants remove twenty-three seeds from a capsule of *C. speciosum* in twelve minutes. Apparently ants consume the edible outer coat, but are deterred by the presence of colchicine from damaging the embryo and cotyledon.

All parts of the common Colchicum, *C. autumnale,* contain an active principle called colchicine.

It was known to the ancients as a dangerous poison, but the corms of other species of Colchicum of Eastern origin enjoyed great reputation in medicine under the name of Hermodactylus.

Theophrastus called it Ephemeron, a name that was supposed by some to signify that the poison killed in a day. The passage describing its effect is somewhat confused, probably from a defective text, and it is not easy to follow his reasoning. He relates that slaves often partook of it when provoked, because there was a well-known antidote for it, and also the death from Colchicum poisoning was slow and lingering, sometimes being delayed for so long as a year, though at times death ensued at once. This seems to imply that the death within a day was not the usual effect, and an offended slave made himself ill by a poison that generally allowed time for recourse to its antidote if circumstances improved.

Dioscorides described the plant and its poisonous qualities. Tragus in 1552 warned his readers against its use in gout, for which it was recommended by the Arabians. Lyte in his translation of Dodonaeus in 1578 writes, 'Meadow or wilde Saffron is corrupt and venomous, therefore not used in medicine,' but Hermodactyl he describes as very good for the 'gowte, the sciatica and all paynes of the joyntes.'

Though Colchicum was mentioned in the London Pharmacopœia of 1618 it was not much valued as a medicine until about the end of the eighteenth century. Then Baron Storck of Vienna called attention to it as a remedy for gout, and it is now recognised as a valuable medicine. Its power of easing pain is said to be due to its effect in checking the circulation, but it is well known that a too frequent use has a terribly lowering effect on the patient. It is interesting to notice how its medicinal reputation has increased while that of Saffron has dwindled and disappeared during the last century.

It is strange that the herbalists who believed in the Doctrine of Signatures overlooked the striking resemblance between a Colchicum corm and a swollen foot. The flat projections from which the shoot proceeds is in some species remarkably like toes, the flattened side represents the sole and the rounded mass the afflicted swollen instep. They firmly believed that walnuts were good for diseases of the head because the outer shell resembles the scalp, the nut shell the skull, and the kernel the folds and convolutions of the brain—but they missed the sign nature had given to the Colchicum.

In recent years a fresh use has been found for the Colchicum; colchicine is now used by cytologists to induce an increase in the number of chromosomes.

The name Colchicum is derived from Colchis in Asia Minor, where the genus is commonly distributed.

It is known in some parts of England as Naked Boys, because the flowers appear without leaves. Parkinson wrote, 'Some have also called them Filius ante Patrem, the Sonne before the

Father, because (as they think) it giveth seed before the flower.'
He then proceeds to show that this is untrue as it flowers in
autumn before the leaves appear and the seeds follow with them
in spring.

The large-flowered species that blossom early in autumn are
easily grown, and so are a few of the spring-flowering forms.
Those that blossom in mid-winter, like *C. variegatum*, are not
easily kept in health, and some beautiful spring-flowering kinds
are difficult to keep alive in the open.

C. speciosum and its varieties are among the handsomest of
bulbous plants and should be in every garden where room can
be spared for the leaves in spring. A rich, deep and rather moist
soil suits most of the species best, but they will thrive in well-
drained slopes of the rock garden also.

CC. autumnale, byzantinum, agrippinum, laetum and *speciosum*
will grow in grass, but in view of their poisonous nature it is
not wise to plant them where cattle graze, and the seed-pods
and leaves should be gathered out if the grass is to be used for
hay.

However, after making many enquiries I have been unable
to learn of a definite case of cattle poisoning by Colchicum,
and it seems probable that beasts avoid eating it just as they
shun buttercups. Colchicums are so plentiful in some parts of
Gloucestershire and also in Alpine pastures that if beasts ate
them cases of poisoning would surely be frequent. I have seen
meadows in the Vésubie Valley, in the Maritime Alps, that
were full of Colchicums, and the leaves and seed-pods were
being cut and dried in the hay; I watched the hay being carried
to the lofts, Colchicums and all. They were so numerous that
it is evident the peasants are not afraid of their poisoning cattle.
It may be that, as with the leaves of Narcissus, which are
regularly gathered and stacked and fed to cows in the Isles of
Scilly, the poisonous qualities disappear with drying.

When planted in grass increase is slow, and as with Crocuses,
if it is desired to obtain a stock, the roots should be planted in
well-tilled ground and divided every second year. In a wild
state the corms of most of the species are found at a great depth,
but in garden ground they do best with the cap of the tunic
reaching the surface.

XVI

Colchicum autumnale and Its Allies

IF we take our wild Colchicum as the starting point of this group of self-coloured flowers we shall find only minor characters to help in distinguishing some of the nearly related ones. All of them are worth growing for their free-flowering habits and to provide a succession of bloom from September to December.

C. autumnale of Linnæus has rather starry segments about two inches in length, of a uniform, soft rose-lilac in the ordinary form. The styles are white and are curved at their summits into crooks which are covered with small papillae, forming the stigmatic surface for the reception of pollen. I have received wild forms from Wiltshire and Norfolk showing slight traces of tessellation in young flowers.

Variety *album* has white flowers, rather smaller than those of the type but so freely produced that it makes a charming plant both in the garden and in grass, flowering later than the rosy form. A white form from Suffolk found near Barham has longer and narrower perianth segments than the plant sold by nurserymen.

Variety *striatum* is more curious than beautiful, with irregularly striped pink and white flowers.

Variety *alboplenum* is an old and very beautiful variety. There is an inferior form in which the flowers are neither so double nor so white as in the better. It should show twenty or more long, narrow, white segments, with just the faintest imaginable flush of pink in their heart. As with other double flowers, the blossoms retain their freshness and beauty longer than the single. When flowering well this good old garden plant is very ornamental in September and October. It is unfortunately rather scarce and always maintains a high price for a Colchicum.

Variety *pleniflorum* has double lilac flowers but an unfortunate habit of blossoming so late in the year that, in most seasons, the cold weather destroys much of its beauty. Should it appear after a spell of sharp frost the flowers are often striped or pied, and at times half lilac and half of a poor, yellowish white.

I have, however, a form found in a cottage garden in Scotland which for the last decade has flowered sufficiently early to escape damage from bad weather and is a very delightful companion for the double white.

There is a very fine figure in Wooster's *Alpine Plants* (1874), vol. I, pl. 18, a full-page plate drawn from a plant grown in Backhouse's nursery at York. It may be a little enlarged, almost to the size of the hybrid variety called 'Waterlily,' but although reproduced by chromolithography the colouring is clear and delicate and worthy of the skill of the artist.

C. atropurpureum of Stapf was described by that great botanist in the 'Cory Volume' of the *Botanical Magazine* in the text to t. 8876 (1938), although the name was published earlier by Mr. W. T. Stearn in *Journal of Botany*, 1934, 341.

It is unfortunate that in the beautiful drawing the two flowers with the tallest tubes and consequently the oldest on the plant are shown as closed and deep purple; hence they appear to have been mistaken by Dr. Stapf for buds. He accordingly declared that 'our plant has small flowers more or less deep reddish purple already in the fully developed bud.'

On that account Stapf discredited my statement that it might be connected with the plant described by Parkinson as *C. atropurpureum* on page 157 of his *Paradisus*, of which he wrote, 'The greatest difference in this kinde consisteth in the flower, which at the first appearance is as pale a purple as the flower of the Hungarian kinde, but after it hath stood in flower two or three days, it beginneth to change, and will after a while become to bee of a very deep reddish purple colour, as also the little foote-stalke whereon it doth stand: the flower is of the bignesse of the Hungarian purple.'

I feel sure that Stapf drew up his description of the bud from the drawings and perhaps never saw an incipient, living bud. In all those I have grown for over a score of years the bud has invariably been white when its tip appears above the soil. It gradually flushes to pale purple, and after two or three days becomes a crimson or magenta shade of purple, redder than in any Colchicum I have seen. The flowers remain rather dwarf, as shown in the open ones of the drawing, and only when fully coloured rise up on the purple tubes.

As recorded in the *Journal R.H.S.*, a plant of *C. atropurpureum* was shown to the Scientific Committee on September 15th, 1942, in which the young flower and its tube were still white, an older one pink and the fully developed one was a deep purple—as described by Parkinson.

Judging by Parkinson's illustrations and descriptions it is difficult to decide what size he intended for what he termed the bignesse of the flower.

It must be borne in mind that most of Parkinson's figures are copied from those in earlier works, frequently coarse and bad copies, altered to fit the space allotted to them. In fig. 5 on page 159, *C. atropurpureum* is represented by an exceptionally bad copy by Switzer of the beautiful illustration in the *Theatrum Florae*, which shows three flowers. Switzer has left out one of them and has joined the tubes of the missing flower to that of the left-hand blossom, which gives it the appearance of a large clumsy flower. Further confusion is caused because the figure is called by Parkinson *C. atropurpureum*, whereas it stands for *C. pannonicum* in the *Theatrum*. The figure of *C. pannonicum* used by Clusius and Lobel is also a different one in Parkinson's *Paradisus*, all show a graceful many-flowered plant with very slender perianth tubes, quite unlike the garbled copy from the *Theatrum*.

If the length of the segments in the *Botanical Magazine* plate is measured and compared with those of Parkinson's fig. 1, page 155 (*C. pannonicum*), they agree exactly.

I think Dr. Stapf founded his belief that Parkinson's *C. atropurpureum* on page 159 had a large flower upon the clumsy figure.

C. atropurpureum was distributed by the firm of Van Tubergen of Haarlem, who received it from the valley of the Meuse. It seems unlikely that a plant with such deep magenta colouring should be a native of that district and to have remained so long overlooked. It may be an escape from some garden, but we know of no species to which it can be referred. Its nearest relative is the Balkan *C. orientale* (*C. turcicum*).

It seems difficult to grow it well and it has died out in this and several other gardens.

C. callicymbium of Stearn and Stefanoff, described in the *Journal of Botany*, 1934, 343, is a very distinct plant cultivated for many years in the Cambridge Botanic Garden under the erroneous name *C. montanum.* Its distinguishing features are a deep purple throat combined with black anthers, by which it can be recognised at a glance. Another clue for its identification is the habit of producing leaves soon after the appearance of the flowers. It comes from Thessaly and Macedonia, and as it is still scarce in gardens let us hope that an ardent botanist will collect it in quantity. The only other Colchicum reputed to have a purple throat and black anthers is the *C. algeriense* described in Battandier and Trabut, *Fl. d'Algerie*, page 76 (1895)=*C. autumnale* var. *algeriense* Battandier and Trabut, *Fl. Anal. d'Alg.*, 336 (1904); previously identified by the same authors in their *Fl. d'Alger, Monocot.*, page 143 (1884), as *C. Bivonae.* This I have never seen, and should very much like an opportunity of comparing it with *C. callicymbium.*

It seems best to deal here with a small group of species resembling one another in having narrow strap-shaped perianth segments, the largest and most widely cultivated of which is *Colchicum laetum* of Steven. A plant has been grown for many years under this name at Glasnevin, from whence I received it, and believe it is rightly named. Stefanoff distinguished it from the group containing *C. autumnale* by the length of the stigmatic surface on the back of the crook: this would be a matter of only a millimetre or so. As a garden plant it is easily recognised by the very distinct form of the flower in which the segments are remarkably strap-shaped and narrow in comparison with their length, producing a flower that is unusually stellate among Colchicums. I can recommend it as a free-flowering easily grown plant, doing well in partial shade or exposed positions.

C. lingulatum of Boissier resembles the last in its narrow segments but differs in flowering much earlier, often in the first weeks of August, and a shorter perianth tube which raises the flowers very little above the soil—I have received it from Mount Parnes and also from a friend in Salonica during the

Kaiser's War, including a very beautiful white variety. The corms are large and bury themselves deeper in the soil than any other species I have.

C. troodi of Kotschy is found only on the Troodos Range in Cyprus, where it is plentiful, especially at Stavros in the Paphos Forest; here it varies a great deal in size and from pale lilac to white. At Prodomos only the small-flowered form occurs. It produces a great number of flowers from a corm. In Cyprus it grows into large clumps, and the crowded flowers, though small, are very charming in early October growing among fallen leaves under the tall trees. Here it makes but little show as I have only a small variety—and the segments are very narrow. The leaves are also small, and so neat for an autumnal-flowering Colchicum that *C. troodi* is a refined little plant for the rock garden. It is figured in the *Botanical Magazine*, t. 6901.

C. Decaisnei of Boissier is another species belonging to this group with strap-shaped flower segments, but until recently its identification with living specimens has been so doubtful that many mistakes arose, as, for instance, when the name was used at Cambridge for *C. cilicicum*.

Dr. Stapf tried to identify the true *C. Decaisnei* of Boissier, but, as reference to his article in the *Botanical Magazine*, t. 9135, will show, he found it an exceedingly difficult problem, which he abandoned without reaching a satisfactory conclusion.

Dr. Post (*Flora of Syria, Palestine and Sinai*, page 808; 1896) included a plant under this name as occurring in Syria and Lebanon. He distinguished it especially by the segments being 'puberulent at the base within.'

Through the kindness of Mrs. McConnel, whose husband was O.C. at Jerusalem during Hitler's War, I obtained specimens recognised as *C. Decaisnei** by Dr. Dinsmore. These included two forms, one with the hairs in the throat described by Dr. Post, and I am now inclined to associate this character with the rounder perianth segments, which make a well-formed and pleasing little flower. The other form has a glabrous throat and rather starry flowers. They are not very satisfactory in our

* Photographs by Mrs. R. McConnel showing these two forms growing in Palestine have been published in *Bull. Alpine Garden Soc.* *10*, 135, 136 (1942).

climate, as they usually flower in November or later and miss the warmth of southern sunshine; however, after the unusually hot summer of 1949 it produced flowers in mid-October which were able to open satisfactorily.

It seems likely that a more extensive comparison of living material of these two forms might justify their recognition as two species, that with the rounder flower and pubescent throat representing Boissier's *C. Decaisnei.*

Three closely allied species are *C. alpinum, C. corsicum* and *C. neapolitanum.* The key given by the Abbé Coste in his *Flore de France* distinguishes them so clearly that I translate it here:

Style straight or scarcely curved at the top, generally shorter than the stamens, which are all inserted at the same level; flowers solitary, generally rather small.

1. *C. alpinum*
Stigmata very short, almost capitate; capsule small, oval, rather long-mucronate, usually surrounded by two leaves; corm small (2 cm. long, 1 cm. wide).

2. *C. corsicum*
Stigmata elongate, club-shaped; capsule larger, oval-oblong, suddenly contracted into a short point, usually surrounded by two leaves; corm larger.

3. *C. neapolitanum*
Style curved or recurved at the top, equalling or more or less longly overtopping the stamens; flowers solitary or two to five fasciculate, large; stigmata curved or slightly crooked; stamens all inserted at the same level; capsule elliptic, the size of a hazel nut, usually surrounded by three linear lanceolate obtuse leaves; corm 2-3 cm. diameter.

4. *C. autumnale*
Stigmata recurved into a hook; the three long stamens inserted higher than the three short ones; capsule oboval, as large as a walnut, usually surrounded by three broadly lanceolate leaves; corm larger.

C. alpinum of de Candolle is one of the most delicately beautiful of autumnal bulbous plants. It is very plentiful in the

Alps, especially on Mont Cenis, at le Lautaret and in Italy, Sicily and Switzerland, but is very seldom seen in cultivation. First of the genus to flower, often appearing in the first days of August, its flowers are about an inch in length and of a uniform rosy lilac.

They are followed in spring, after the melting of the snow, by two narrow leaves, that if once recognised as belonging to this desirable species are an easy guide to its corm. Fortunately it does not grow so troublesomely deep in the soil as is the habit of its relatives. I have not found it very easy to grow, and perhaps there is something lacking in our conditions that fails to compensate it for the long resting period under the snow of its alpine home. It is worth looking out for when collecting in the Alps and trying in various soils and positions at home until success is assured.

C. guadarramense of Pau is the name applied at Kew to a charming little species that came to me some years ago from the mountains of Asturias in northern Spain. It greatly resembles *C. alpinum* but flowers in September quite a month later, is rather larger in flower and a great deal larger as regards its more numerous leaves.

The stiff, solid little segments of the flowers are of a charmingly warm shade of pink, and the plant promises to be quite at home in the lower beds of the rock garden. Willkomm and Lange mention a plant in their *Prodromus Florae Hispanicae* found near Guadarrama as being akin to *C. arenarium*, a Hungarian species not in cultivation. According to Pau it is this Spanish species which was at that time very imperfectly known to them.

C. corsicum of Baker is much like *C. alpinum*, but differs in longer stigmata and larger corms and seedpods. It is peculiar to siliceous soils in the mountains of Corsica and is not in general cultivation.

C. neapolitanum of Tenore is found in parts of southern France as well as in Italy. It is a small-flowered species, very much like *C. autumnale*, but is distinct in that the anthers are all inserted at the same level, whereas in most other Colchicums they are set in two ranks.

XVII

Colchicum cilicicum and C. byzantinum

C. cilicicum of Dammer was figured and described by Stapf in the *Botanical Magazine*, t. 9135 (1928), in which article he stated that this is the correct name for the plant grown for many years as "*C. Decaisnei*" at Cambridge and elsewhere and frequently illustrated in journals under that name. As it is a large and handsome-flowered plant it is curious that it should ever have been associated with the small-flowered Syrian species described on page 165. It was received at Cambridge from Siehe of Mersina, who collected it in the Cilician Taurus. Imported corms vary considerably in size of leaves and width of segments of the flowers. The form grown at Cambridge has wider and altogether larger leaves as compared with others more recently imported, which mostly have more starry flowers and narrower leaves. The leaves of this species are, with the exception of *C. callicymbium*, always the first to appear in autumn after the fading of the flowers.

C. cilicicum is a very desirable and handsome garden plant, producing a long succession of flowers, and it has no fads as to position or soil. This species has also been collected by Mr. G. P. Baker in the Sultan Dagh, when he was on his way to Tarsus. Var. *purpureum* has rich red-purple flowers.

C. byzantinum was so named by Clusius in his *Plantarum Historia* in 1601 because, as he wrote, its peculiar corms were sent from Constantinople in 1588 to two Viennese ladies, from whom he received offsets when he was living in Vienna. Linnæus omitted it in his *Species Plantarum*, and thus the name was not validly established until 1807, when Ker-Gawler published it in a synopsis of Colchicum species under t. 1028 of the *Botanical Magazine*.

A year later it was figured in the *Botanical Magazine*, t. 1122, in a fine illustration drawn by Sydenham Edwards with his wonderful skill for showing the principal characters of a plant on an octavo page. In this instance the strongly crooked stigma, rather short straight filaments and enormously wide leaf are so clearly displayed that I am convinced it represents the plant widely grown in gardens as *C. byzantinum*.

Stapf was inclined to sink *C. byzantinum* under *C. cilicicum*, but I feel sure that if he had been able to compare living specimens of both he would have found sufficient evidence to justify treating them as separate species. The styles of *C. byzantinum* only slightly overtop the stamens and are tipped with a very conspicuous crimson crook. The filaments of the stamens are only half as long as the perianth segments and are scarcely curved, and the anthers stand erect and are a dull yellow in colour.

On the other hand in *C. cilicicum* the styles are longer and almost as long as the perianth-segments. They are not crooked at the tip and terminate in a punctiform or slightly oblique dull purple stigma. The filaments are also long, they diverge sharply outwards at their point of insertion and then curve slightly inwards in their upper portion and thus provide space for the anthers to lie horizontally, and as these are of a remarkably bright yellow they are very conspicuous, even from a distance. The flowers vary from dark rosy lilac to purple, in *C. byzantinum* they are a pale pinkish lilac.

It is characteristic of *C. cilicicum* that the outer sheath reaches right up to the surface of the soil and is usually clearly visible in the short interval between the fading of the flowers and the appearance of the leaves. In *C. byzantinum* as in most other species, with the exception of *C. lusitanum*, the sheath is not normally visible above the soil at any stage.

These two plants also differ in their normal times of leafing and flowering. As stated on page 168, *C. cilicicum* produces leaves soon after the flowers fade, and they are generally large enough to be conspicuous before the end of the year, whereas those of *C. byzantinum* do not appear before the spring. As regards the period of flowering the sequence is reversed, for *C. byzantinum* flowers with *C. autumnale* in August and is generally over by the time the first flowers of *C. cilicicum* appear.

Again *C. cilicicum* seeds freely and seedlings vary in form and colour, but *C. byzantinum* of late years has not been noticed to seed, and the garden stock now grown is almost certainly one clone, which increases so freely by multiplication of the corms that, like other garden plants, it may have become sterile— Clusius wrote of the plant he described that it bore seed fairly copiously and included a figure showing leaves and capsules. Those now grown may be descended from his form, as the 350 years of vegetative propagation should be a sufficient period for the change. In all characters except the failure to produce seeds our garden plant agrees fully with Clusius's admirably complete and clear description.

The only discrepancy between the *Botanical Magazine* figure and a living flower is the absence of the crimson tip of the stigma, perhaps due to its omission by the colorist of the plate.

The corm of *C. byzantinum* is the largest of the genus and so irregular in shape that it has been likened to a doubled fist. The leaves are on a scale to match the corm, sometimes six inches in width and a foot in length, and are strongly ribbed or pleated, and when half grown they look much like those of a Veratrum. Clusius likened them to White Hellebore, *Helleborus albus* of his date, now *Veratrum album*. Nurserymen's lists sometimes contain a *Colchicum veratrifolium*, which is really this handsome plant.

A form with variegated leaves was grown at one time, but I have not seen it lately. The variegation consisted of a whitish margin but was not sufficiently well defined to be handsome.

It is one of the most floriferous species, producing as many as twenty flowers from one corm. Their segments are about two inches in length, rounded and a pale rose-lilac in colour. There is no hardier or more easily grown species, and were it not for the immensity of its foliage it should be planted by hundreds to provide a rosy carpet of flowers in September.

XVIII

Colchicum speciosum and Its Varieties

C. speciosum of Steven bears the largest and handsomest flowers
of the genus. They stand up boldly on their perianth tubes,
which, when fully developed, reach nearly a foot in length.
Some four or more inches of the tube are below ground,
according to the depth of planting. Allowing for that the
flowers are taller than those of other Colchicums and resemble
Tulips in appearance.

Their form is globose, tapering gradually to the tube, and
the rounded segments are about four inches in length and in
the best forms nearly three in width. As many as four flowers
are sometimes produced by a flowering shoot, and such a
free-flowering, handsome plant makes a good show in the
garden in the early half of October.

The typical form came first from the Caucasus, the original
description by Steven being made from plants introduced
from thence about 1828, but various forms are now known, as
the species has a wide range in the Caucasus, Asia Minor and
north Persia.

It seeds freely in gardens and the seedlings vary in size and
colour and there are already too many names applied to
somewhat similar varieties. This is almost certain to happen
when a handsome plant begins to vary in different gardens,
and when once a name has found a place in a trade list it is
seldom dislodged. The result is that there will be as many names
as purchasers will pay for.

The original plant can be distinguished by the deep lilac
colour of the tube and the white markings of its throat. On
their first appearance above ground the tubes may be cream
colour, flushed with lilac, but they deepen with age. The white
of the throat passes gradually into the lilac, but a distinct white
point runs up the centre of each segment for about an inch
beyond the highest point of the white on the margins. A curious

scent can be noticed in this form, rather like that of a ripe plum, but with a whiff of something unpleasant underlying it, slightly ammoniacal and like that of a stable.

Some outstanding varieties were raised in Messrs. Backhouse's celebrated nurseries at York, ranging from white to rich ruby-purple.

This pure white variety, *C. speciosum album,* is one of the most beautiful of hardy bulbous plants. The snow-white goblets of good form, equal to that of a Tulip, standing on soft emerald-green tubes, cannot be equalled for beauty in the late autumn by any other plant so easy to grow well in the open. Its only rivals among white flowers are *Romneya Coulteri* and *Crinum Powellii album,* which, however, have generally left the field clear for the Colchicum before its flowering season commences.

The first roots that were sold changed hands at the price of five guineas each.

It requires a little more attention here than the ordinary forms, and I find it best to replant the corms every second year. At Earlham Hall, Norwich, it throve so well in light but good soil that six roots increased to five hundred in ten years.

On the other hand, at Leith Vale, Ockley, it has flourished and increased equally well in stiff clay.

Many dark purple forms have been selected and named. I think the best are the two listed as *rubrum* and *atrorubens* which are so much alike that even when growing close together I sometimes have to look at their labels to be certain to which stocks they belong. Perhaps *rubrum* is rather paler and in some seasons flowers a little earlier. Both are very valuable for planting near other Colchicums, for the contrast of their rich purple tones against the rosy lilac shades of paler forms, and planted in a mass their colour effect is almost the same on the ground as that of *Lespedeza bicolor* overhead.

In the late afternoon when the red rays of the low sun reach them the blue and lilac tones disappear and the rosy and red tones are flattered and enhanced; these purple Colchicums then glow like garnets and are marvellously beautiful. Also they are astonishingly brilliant under lamplight in the house.

I bought a very large, rosy purple variety as *maximum* from Smith of Newry many years ago. It has not increased here as well as I could wish, and I hope it may have done better with others, as it is a handsome late-flowering kind.

'Ruby Queen' has only lately arrived here from a garden in Suffolk, where the large flowers stood up on tall tubes.

They open widely and display the pleasant contrast of a conspicuously white throat with an unusually bright rosy lilac upper half of the broad segments.

The late R. O. Backhouse, of Sutton Court, Hereford, besides raising many fine Daffodils and the Marhan race of hybrid Lilies, also produced some seedlings of *C. speciosum* with flowers of a remarkably strong substance and segments so broad and rounded that they are almost as wide as long, and their shape is like that of a prize-winning old English Tulip, two-thirds of a sphere. Of these, that named 'Huxley' is the best and largest; in depth of colour it is almost as dark as *atrorubens*, which matches with the R.H.S. colour chart; both are Petunia Purple of sheet 118. *Atrorubens* agrees best with the darkest tone 32 and the deepest portion of 'Huxley' with the lighter tone 32/1.

A paler seedling named 'Darwin' is smaller but so globular and rosy that it is a worthy companion for 'Huxley.' It matches 32/2 of the R.H.S. colour chart on the same sheet as the last.

Some confusion exists in the names of *Bornmuelleri, giganteum* and *illyricum* when applied to some large-flowered Colchicums in gardens.

C. speciosum var. *Bornmuelleri* of Bergmans, although originally described as a species *C. Bornmuelleri* by Freyn, is no more than a larger and earlier-flowering form of *C. speciosum*. It first flowered in cultivation in 1889, corms having been collected that year by Joseph F. N. Bornmüller on the mountains near Amasia in Asia Minor. This variety differs from the type *C. speciosum* in flowering a week or more earlier and in the colour of the perianth tube, which is green and never becomes tinted with purple, as always happens with the coloured forms of *C. speciosum*.

The first to come here with the name *Bornmuelleri* is easily recognised by the flower buds being white when they push through the soil. After a day or two they are mottled or striped with lilac and when mature the lilac spreads all over the segments, except in the throat, which remains conspicuously white.

Messrs. Van Tubergen raised a seedling and named it
C. Bornmuelleri magnificum, with larger flowers rosy lilac in the
bud stage.

It also has a pale green tube, and in both the white markings
of the throat rise higher at the margins of each segment than
in the centre, which adds to the size and beauty of the white
surface.

In the text accompanying t. 9135 (*C. cilicicum*) of the *Botanical
Magazine* Dr. Stapf wrote, 'Stefanoff's wide concept of
C. speciosum as *cilicicum* and *Balansae* does not seem to me
maintainable.'

In the next line he stated that t. 6078 does not represent
C. speciosum but *C. Bornmuelleri*.

However, in both the figure and the text the perianth tube
is shown to be purple, and the white of the throat does not rise
higher than the sides of the segments, therefore I consider
the plate correctly represents *C. speciosum*. Until we have
fresh stocks from their native habitats to grow together
for comparison we cannot decide their status as species or
varieties.

In 1916 Messrs. Barr showed a Colchicum under the name
C. illyricum superbum, which received an award of merit from the
Royal Horticultural Society and was figured in the *Gardeners'
Magazine* for October 21st, 1916. This photograph very clearly
shows the remarkable form of the flowers, which differ from all
other species. It should be called *C. giganteum*.

All varieties of *C. speciosum* have flowers which can be
described as shaped like a Tulip, with broad segments remaining
concave on the upper surface. In *C. giganteum* the segments
open out more widely and remain expanded at an angle of
forty-five degrees, almost flat on the upper surface but with a
tendency to be twisted towards the apex, and they resemble a
Lily or Hippeastrum rather than a Tulip.

It is a very distinct and beautiful plant, a strong grower,
increasing well and flowering freely rather later than *C. speciosum*,
which makes it valuable for lengthening the season of large-
flowered Colchicums.

An early large-flowered form is sometimes labelled *C. speciosum*

giganteum in gardens which I believe is Van Tubergen's seedling
C. Bornmuelleri magnificum.

The legitimate claimant to this name of *C. giganteum* was
introduced by Max Leichtlin, of Baden-Baden, who during the
last decade of the nineteenth century until his death in 1910
issued short lists of new or rare plants which he received from
collectors working mostly in the Near East. Through the kindness of Mr. John Hoog of Haarlem, who has a complete
set of those lists, I learn that Leichtlin first offered it in
his printed list for 1890 as '*C. giganteum* (?) introduced from
Kurdistan, flowers similar to those of *C. speciosum,* not
warranted.'

It was omitted from the next three lists, but was included
again in 1894 and 1895 without description.

In 1896 Leichtlin added 'stronger and larger than *speciosum,*'
and included it in the yearly lists as late as 1903. As shown by a
pencil note in Mr. John Hoog's handwriting, six corms were
purchased from the 1894 list. It was offered in Messrs. Van
Tubergen's catalogue for the first time in 1902, and was still
offered in 1938, described as 'dark lilac, large flower, late
flowering (identical with *C. illyricum superbum*).'

The first reference to *Colchicum giganteum* in English horticultural literature occurs in an article by Samuel Arnott in the
Gardeners' Chronicle (iii), *32*, 435 (December 1902).

Arnott grew a great number of rare bulbs in his garden in
Dumfries and wrote interesting notes, many of which are
valuable records of their origin and introduction. In this article
he states that he received it from Max Leichtlin in the summer
of 1901. Evidently he did not consider it so fine a plant as
C. speciosum or *C. Bornmuelleri,* but noted that when these were
over 'it is the tallest and largest of the genus in bloom; its colour
is pleasing, being of a soft rosy-purple, while the flowers are
of good substance, and held erect on stout tubes which stand
the weather well. The foliage produced in spring and lasting
for a while in summer is large and effective.' Although close to
C. speciosum 'its later blooming, its softer colouring, and the less
marked white at the base of the segments mark it out as at least
a distinct variety.'

Messrs. Barr obtained it about the same time and George

Moon made a beautiful drawing of it at their Long Ditton nursery, which is included in the beautiful plate of Colchicums, facing page 108 of *Flora and Sylva*, *1* (1903).

The two outstanding characters of *C. giganteum*, viz. the distinct open shape and the height of the flowers, are clearly shown. G. Mallet, who wrote the accompanying text, did not refer to it, and the editor (W. Robinson) added, 'The plant named *C. giganteum* in our drawing has lately come into cultivation under this name in several nurseries, and is a fine large kind, but what affinity it has to others previously known we cannot at present tell.'

John Weathers in his *Bulb Book*, 146 (1911), described *C. giganteum* as 'a fine species of the *speciosum* group from the Zigana Dagh, or Gypsy Mountain, bearing very large and handsome blossoms of a delicate soft rose shading to white at the base,' and referred to *Flora and Sylva*; this statement as to the provenance of *C. giganteum* has been repeated in Messrs. R. W. Wallace's catalogues from 1922 onwards. Probably *C. giganteum* came from the mountains around the Zigana Pass about thirty miles south-west of Trabzon in north-eastern Turkey.

Later the name *C. illyricum* was used for it, possibly because Mr. P. R. Barr received corms said to have come from Macedonia.

It was thought that they might be *C. illyricum* of Frivaldsky, which Baker mentioned under *C. speciosum* as a Macedonian plant, either the same or closely related.

Macedonia and Illyria are both too far outside the range of *C. speciosum* to include any form of it.

The combination *C. illyricum* has an interesting but unfortunate history, having been erroneously applied by authors to many very distinct Colchicums.

The epithet *illyricum* (referring to Illyricum, the eastern or Balkan coast of the Adriatic Sea) was first associated with a Colchicum by Matthias de l'Obel in his *Plantarum seu Stirpium Historia*, 73 (1576); here under the heading *Hermodactyli; non venenati officinarum* l'Obel described a species received in a dry state from Aleppo which had numerous fascicled spreading leaves and very small yellowish flowers. This was undoubtedly the plant now called *Colchicum fasciculare*, although his artist seems to have interpreted it as a bulbous plant with a short stem thickly covered by leaves out of whose axils there arose short-stalked flowers. L'Obel named it *Colchicum Illyricum sive Graecum non venenatum Anguillarae*, thereby confusing it with a Balkan species briefly mentioned as 'Colchico' in Luigi Anguillara's *Semplici*, 275 (1561). Gerard, in his *Herball*, 129 (1597), copied l'Obel's misleading woodcut and rendered the identity of the plant yet further obscure by calling it '*Colchicum Illiricum*: Greeke medow Saffron.' Himself misled by the figure, Gerard then said: 'The medow Saffron of Illiria hath a greate, thicke, and bulbus roote, full of substance: from which riseth up a fat, thicke, and grosse stalke, set about from the lower part to the top by equall distances, with long, thicke, and grosse leaves, sharp pointed, not unlike to the leaves of Leekes: among which leaves do grow yellowish flowers like unto the English medow Saffron, but smaller.' Later authors can be excused for failing to recognise the little Aleppo Colchicum as the origin of this remarkable description! Other pre-Linnæan writers also used the name *Colchicum illyricum* without adding to our knowledge of the plant concerned. It was taken up by Dr. Jonathan Stokes in his *Botanical Materia Medica*, 2, 329 (1812), and associated with the Aleppo plant. Meanwhile in 1756 a beautiful engraving of this plant, after a drawing by G. D. Ehret, had appeared in A. Russell, *Natural History of Aleppo*, t. 2, facing page 34 (1756), under the name *Allium Sylvestre sive moly minus*.

Linnæus, who knew the plant only from this illustration, supposed it to be a species of Hypoxis, and named it *H. fascicularis* in 1759. Later, in 1826, Robert Brown with his usual acuteness recognised it as a species of Colchicum and renamed it *C. fasciculare*, which remains its correct title. Hence the name *C. illyricum* of Stokes is a synonym of *C. fasciculare*, and can never be legitimately used for any other plant.

The next use of the name *C. illyricum* was by the Hungarian plant collector Imre Frivaldsky, who attached it about 1840 to specimens of a Colchicum gathered by him in Macedonia. It was not validly published, but merely cited, by Kunth in

M

1842 and by Baker in 1879 as a doubtful herbarium name under *C. speciosum*, with which it assuredly had no connection.

All varieties of *C. speciosum* are good for indoor decoration, and when gathered will last for nearly a week in a bowl, either with or without water. They are particularly beautiful by artificial light, which enhances the red tints of the blossoms.

XIX

Tessellated Species

IN most kinds of Colchicums the colour of the segments is more or less uniform throughout, but generally rather paler towards the throat; though longitudinal veins are present their visibility is only due to the thickening of vascular tissue and not to the presence of pigment. In some, however, the surface is further divided into rectangular patches by the presence of small coloured cross-veins. Parkinson translated Clusius's apt description as 'with some veines or markes upon the flowers making some shew of a chequer on the outside, but not so conspicuous as in the true chequered kinds.' This can be seen in the freshly opened flowers of *C. byzantinum*.

A further development occurs when every alternate square is suffused with a deeper colour; this results in a chequered pattern which goes by the name of tessellation, and is much like that found in our wild fritillary, *Fritillaria Meleagris*.

It is most marked in *C. variegatum*, also known as *C. Parkinsonii* from the woodcut in Parkinson's *Paradisus*. The chequers in this flower are deep crimson and almost pure white. In other forms the markings vary somewhat according to the age of the flowers, and in some they are only distinct in a young blossom.

C. Sibthorpii of Baker is beautifully figured as *C. latifolium* in t. 350 of Sibthorp and Smith's *Flora Graeca*, but unfortunately the flowering specimen illustrated was associated with the description of the leaves of *C. byzantinum latifolium polyanthes* of Clusius, which is quite a different plant. Baker therefore considered it best to drop the name *C. latifolium* and to rename the plant after Sibthorp. This course receives confirmation from the modern Rules of Nomenclature, under which *C. latifolium* must be classed as an illegitimate name by reason of the inclusion of the synonym taken from Clusius, which was already at that time the type of the name *C. byzantinum* Ker-Gawler.

I collected a plant which I take as the true *C. Sibthorpii* on the hillsides near Tatoi, below Mount Parnes, the same spot where I first saw the Grecian *Crocus aureus* in flower; it is undoubtedly the same as specimens in the Kew herbarium collected on Parnes by Heldreich, which were amongst those forming the basis of Baker's description. This plant has blossomed for a number of years in my garden, appearing above ground in September or October. In the shape of its lightly tessellated flowers it agrees well with Sibthorp's plate; the leaves, which until 1951 had never been properly described, are of a somewhat dull bluish-green colour and wavy on the margins; when full grown they are less than an inch wide, nearly six inches long and spread horizontally.

Baker later attached the name *C. Sibthorpii* to a very distinct plant illustrated in the *Botanical Magazine*, t. 7181 (1891); this shows a larger, more globular flower with richer colouring than in my Tatoi plant, and has decidedly different leaves. When young these are of a richer green and are almost erect, not spreading and scarcely at all wavy on the margins. They grow to a larger size, over an inch wide and ten inches long, and remain erect when full grown; about nine leaves are produced, which is a high number for any species of Colchicum.

The flowers, several to a corm, are of good shape with pointed tipped segments about two inches in length. They vary a good deal in the intensity of the dark squares and are not evenly chequered all over. The general colour of the ground and chequers deepens with the age of the flower.

The plants originally introduced soon died out both here and in Holland, being apparently rather tender late-flowering forms seldom appearing above ground before the end of November. Another stock, which I received from the hills behind Salonica, has so far proved hardier and is the form represented in plate 28.

The differences between this plant from northern Greece and the Tatoi Colchicum, which is to be taken as true *C. Sibthorpii*, are so great that they must be regarded as distinct species; the plant from Salonica has therefore been described by Burtt as *C. Bowlesianum* in *Kew Bull.* 1950, 433 (1951.)

The most remarkable of all these tessellated Colchicums is that recently described by Burtt (*loc. cit.*) as *C. macrophyllum.*

It was collected by the late Hiatt C. Baker on one of his excursions to Crete. It has the largest leaf of any Colchicum I have ever seen and would well deserve the names of *latifolium* or *veratrifolium* were they not already used for other Colchicums. The uppermost leaf can reach a height of two feet and the larger leaves may be over a foot long and nearly half as broad. The leaves are conspicuously pleated after the manner of a Veratrum and might easily be thought to belong to that genus. This species is, in fact, a very ornamental foliage plant provided it be given adequate space for its full development.

The flowers are decidedly funnel-shaped, without the distinctly curved outline of *C. Sibthorpii* and *C. Bowlesianum*, the segments are oblong, about two and three-quarter inches by seven-eighths of an inch wide, tapering only in the upper quarter to a bluntish tip; the rather narrow segments give a starry appearance to the open flower. The ground colour is very pale lilac, nearly white, and the tessellations are faintly and rather vaguely marked, and of a pallid lilac colour. The filaments are white and the orange blotch near the base is well developed. The connective of the young anthers is white, tinged with lilac, and the flanges are of a dull putty colour; after dehiscence they are covered with green pollen, a most unusual feature among Colchicums. The styles are curved at the apex, but taper off smoothly without the clublike swelling found in *C. Sibthorpii* and *C. Bowlesianum*, the styles are white but the stigmatic ridges become lilac at maturity.

The style exceeds the insertion of the anther on the filament by three-quarters of an inch in the longer stamens of mature flowers and by an inch with regard to the lower stamens.

Herbarium specimens of this fine Colchicum have recently been collected near Retymo by Messrs. Barneby and Davis, and it is the same plant which was distributed as *C. variegatum* in the early part of the last century by the botanist-traveller Sieber.

A plant similar in all respects except size was collected by Mr. Ogilvie-Grant in Rhodes. It flowered for the first time in this country in 1948 and was distinctly smaller, both in flower and in leaf, than Mr. Hiatt Baker's Cretan introduction. The Rhodes has so far flowered about three weeks earlier than the Cretan form. That the plants from Crete and Rhodes belong to the same species has been made clear from a comparison of the living plants in Myddelton House garden where the plant from Crete (collected by Mr. H. C. Baker) and that from Rhodes (collected by Mr. Ogilvie-Grant) grow within a few yards of one another. The leaves are nine inches long and four inches broad. Despite these differences there is no doubt that Mr. Ogilvie-Grant's plant must be referred to as *C. macrophyllum*.

C. variegatum of Linnæus is the correct name for *C. Parkinsonii* Ker-Gawler and the subject to t. 6090 (1874) of the *Botanical Magazine*.

It has been confused with the more easily grown and commoner species *C. agrippinum*, but can be easily distinguished when in blossom by the much more distinct chequering of the flower, by the shape of the three outer segments, which are an inch wide near the base and then taper to a sharp point, and by the absence of any orange spot at the base of the white filaments.

When the leaves of the two are compared it will be seen that *C. variegatum* as Linnæus described it has the fewer leaves, and that they spread on the ground with markedly waved edges. In *C. agrippinum* the leaves stand nearly upright and their margins are only slightly waved.

C. variegatum is found in Greece and the islands of the Archipelago, but though it has frequently been brought to our gardens ever since Parkinson's day it is not often seen in them. It is an uncertain plant here, generally attempting to flower in mid-December an being frustrated by some adverse spell of weather. The flowers are raised so little above the soil that they fall an easy prey to slugs.

In spite of these drawbacks, as Parkinson wrote, 'yet when it flowereth anything earlie that it may have any comfort of a warm sun, it is the glorie of all these kinds.'

C. agrippinum is a name adopted by Baker from garden usage for a plant also known as *C. tessellatum*, and it has also been miscalled *C. variegatum* or *C. Parkinsonii*. Like *C. variegatum* it has chequered flowers and purple anthers, but differs in the less pronouced, almost smudgy, effect of the tessellation and in the shape of its perianth segments, which only exceed half an inch in width in the largest flowers and taper to rather blunt point.

What appears to be a superior form has lately been listed as *C. Parkinsonii*, but except in size of both flowers and leaves it agrees fully with the widely cultivated *C. agrippinum* of gardens. The *Botanical Magazine*, t. 1028, represents this plant well in all characters except the anthers, which are shown as yellow. This may have resulted from the drawing having been made from a mature flower after the pollen had covered the purple skin of the anther. There is an orange spot at the base of each of the crimson filaments, and this produces a rich glowing effect of colour at the throat of a mature blossom which is very noticeable and unlike that of any other Colchicum. This species was figured as *C. variegatum* by Redouté (*Liliacées*, 4, t. 238; 1808), though the colour is somewhat too pale.

The flowers of *C. agrippinum* appear early, frequently in the end of August, rise on long perianth tubes and are numerous from each corm, in strong contrast with the dwarf, late and few flowers of *C. variegatum*. I have never noticed any seed vessels, and this suggests a hybrid origin and makes us wonder whether *C. variegatum* could have been crossed with *C. autumnale* and have produced this easily grown and showy garden plant, the native country of which is unknown. In some parts of Suffolk and Surrey *C. agrippinum* has become established in orchards and pastures, which bears witness to the vigour of its vegetative reproduction and supports the supposed presence of *C. autumnale* in its parentage.

C. Bivonae of Gussone I have not seen alive. The only material in the Kew herbarium that can be accepted with confidence comes from Sicily and has very long narrow leaves. Although many authors have attributed a very wide distribution to this plant I can find no trustworthy evidence of this.

C. lusitanum of Brotero, which Willkomm and Lange called *C. Bivonae* in their *Prodromus Florae Hispanicae*, has recently been illustrated in the *Botanical Magazine* (n.s., t. 21; 1948) from material sent to me by Mr. Edwards, gardener at Government House, Gibraltar. The flowers vary much in the amount of tessellation; they are larger and more handsome than those of *C. autumnale*, and appearing later they are a valuable addition to autumn-flowering species. The leaves are similar to those of *C. autumnale*.

C. Tenorii of Parlatore is an Italian species found near Naples. I believe I have the plant here as described by Baker from specimens in the late H. J. Elwes' garden in Gloucestershire. As I know it, it stands half-way between a tessellated form such as *C. agrippinum* and the rosy concolorous forms of *C. autumnale*, being slightly tessellated and in shape like *C. autumnale*. A point which catches the eye and easily distinguishes the flowers from those of *C. autumnale* is the crimson colour of the stigmatic crook, which is continued for a little way down the style.

XX

Garden-Raised Hybrids

THOUGH there are good reasons for believing that *CC. byzantinum* and *agrippinum* may have arisen under cultivations we have no definite evidence of any deliberate attempt to cross different species earlier than the commencement of the present century.

Mr. Thomas Hoog, of Haarlem, has kindly furnished the following facts.

There was in Haarlem a nursery owned by Messrs. Zocher and Co. which has by now entirely disappeared. Sometime between 1900 and 1905 Mr. J. J. Kerbert, the head of the firm, was very successful in raising a great number of good seedlings, the result of crossing the forms then known in gardens as *Colchicum Bornmuelleri* and *giganteum* with the large-flowered chequered species from Greece, at that time supposed to be *C. Sibthorpii* of Baker, but actually the plant from which were drawn t. 7181 of the *Botanical Magazine* and G. Moon's beautiful plate in *Flora and Sylva*, vol. 1, 108, now to be called *C. Bowlesianum*. As mentioned in the preceding chapter, that importation proved too tender for outdoor cultivation and died out both in Holland and in Britain, but it has been exceedingly useful in supplying pollen to produce a remarkably beautiful race of chequered Cochicums of great vigour and hardiness.

The same firm used the pollen of the double-flowered *C. autumnale album* on *C. speciosum album*, from which cross the enormous pink, double-flowered variety 'Waterlily' was obtained.

A great number, perhaps too many, of these Zocher seedlings were named and distributed by several Dutch firms.

Some are so much alike that it is possible stocks of one variety may have passed into different hands and then received distinct names.

Messrs. Van Tubergen offered some of the best and Messrs.

Van Meeuwen issued a very good coloured plate showing one of the parent plants as *C. Bornmuelleri* and the hybrids 'Lilac Wonder,' 'Violet Queen,' 'Conquest' and 'Waterlily.'

Another coloured plate, not nearly so good, was published in *Gartenschönheit*, 1938, facing page 388. It contains 'Lilac Wonder,' 'General Grant,' 'The Giant,' 'Violet Queen' and 'Danton.'

A short but valuable note on these hybrids by R. E. Arnold in *Gardening Illustrated* for September 12th, 1941, drew attention to their beauty and interest in gardens; but they have never been planted so widely and freely as their hardiness, earliness and freedom of flowering should have ensured, and they are not frequently listed by nurserymen.

Mr. F. J. Chittenden wisely and fortunately obtained all the varieties procurable when he was the director of Wisley, and they have thrived and increased well in the light soil, and now provide remarkably fine masses of varied shades of lovely rosy lilac to purple through August and September among shrubs in the Azalea garden.

As they have grown in my garden they may be arranged in groups according to colour markings and period of flowering.

In the first group are those in which the globular form and conspicuous tessellation of the Grecian parent predominate. They also inherited the red and purple flanges of the anthers together with a flush of lilac colouring on the style which deepens with age.

The richly chequered varieties can be subdivided into those with early or later flowering periods.

In normal seasons with good rains in July three varieties generally produce flowers early in August; they are the first of the larger-flowered Colchicums of the season and are very bright and strikingly conspicuous on the bare earth, especially in afternoon sunshine. They are 'Princess Astrid,' 'Rubens' and 'Autumn Queen' (A.M., Haarlem, 1926); their flowering periods are so simultaneous and they resemble each other so much that I can find no character by which to separate them, and suspect that they may be one original stock bearing different names. Anyway they are very charming and easily grown, and there is no harm in having all three if they are still procurable;

one of them should be in every garden. There is a brighter tint of bluish lilac in their flowers when seen in a mass than in any early form of *C. autumnale* or *C. byzantinum.*

These are followed in mid-September by 'Disraeli,' a large flower of great substance, with segments slightly waved at the margins and hooded at the apex, like those of *C. Bowlesianum,* which it greatly resembles in size and conspicuous chequering. It received the A.M., Haarlem, in 1931.

'Glory of Heemstede' has a larger, more starry funnel-shaped flower. Cream-coloured filaments deepening to yellow bases are a feature of this variety and add to the effect of the closely tessellated bright rosy pattern.

'Violet Queen' also has long pointed segments closely tessellated on a bluish lilac ground contrasting pleasantly with the conspicuously white throat and central channels of the segments.

Among the latest to flower of my Dutch hybrids are two called 'Danton' and 'Conquest,' the deepest coloured and handsomest of the tessellated forms, but so much alike that after many seasons of observation I am unable to describe any characters sufficiently distinct to serve in recognising either without the other for comparison. 'Conquest' is the better known now and 'Danton' is seldom listed.

I think 'Danton' should be rather darker, rounder in outline and with a more distinctly defined white throat, but an extra large fresh bloom of 'Conquest' sometimes seems more handsome than a secondary one of 'Danton,' and it may be another instance of two names for one seedling. Flowering later and lasting to the end of September, whichever name it bears, it is the best of the tessellated hybrids.

'President Coolidge' differs very little from the last; perhaps we can say it is rather redder in tone; the tessellation is less distinct and the white of the throat extends higher up the inside of the segments.

The second group evidently resembles the plain lilac parent more than the chequered one in the greater size of the long firm tube, the taller and smoother segments of the tulip-shaped flowers, and also very slight tessellation which shows mostly on the inner surface.

Two outstanding varieties of this group, 'The Giant' (F.C.C., Haarlem, 1931) and 'Premier,' are so robust and large that they are good for planting between shrubs or in rough grass— but they are more brightly coloured when grown in full sunlight.

'Beaconsfield' is smaller but similar in colouring and form.

'Dandaels' fits in here because although it has a globular flower with wide, rounded segments, there are some conspicuous tessellation spots on the inner surface forming a ring just above the tops of the anthers; otherwise it is a self shade of very pale lilac. Here it ripens seeds freely, and so far is the only one of these hybrids to do so.

The last group may be called the 'Lilac Wonder' set, to connect it with the best known and most characteristic of the varieties with long, more or less narrow segments, in which traces of tessellation are very slight and only consist of an outlining by small cross veins which give the appearance of a fine network pattern, especially on the lower and outer portions of the outer segments. This feature was first described by Clusius in his account of *C. byzantinum*, and Parkinson's English translation of it is mentioned in the preceding chapter.

'Lilac Wonder' (F.C.C., Haarlem, 1927) and 'Mr. Kerbert' are much alike in general appearance, but can be recognised as distinct by comparing the amount of white in throat and styles.

In 'Lilac Wonder' the white of the throat can only be seen if the segments are forced open at the base, and it is completely hidden when they are in their natural position.

In 'Mr. Kerbert' the throat is conspicuously white and above that a well-marked white channel continues up to two-thirds of the length of the segments.

In 'Lilac Wonder' the channel is very narrow and shorter and the style is white, whereas in 'Mr. Kerbert' the style is lilac.

The segments are two and three-quarter inches long in both but narrower by an eighth of an inch, more rosy and more conspicuously marked with cross veins in 'Lilac Wonder' than in 'Mr. Kerbert.'

They are free flowering and very effective in a good clump,

as the starry segments of the crowded blossoms contrast pleasantly with cup-shaped varieties. 'Lilac Wonder' has a very long and slender perianth-tube and the flowers generally fall over on their second day, but open widely while lying on the ground, and last for several days if slugs and caterpillars fail to discover them.

I have no reliable information as to their parentage, and as the trace of tessellation is so slight and the segments so narrow it seems unlikely that *C. Bowlesianum* was used. It may be that they are akin to 'Waterlily,' which has segments much like theirs in form and colour.

I grew three forms which differ from the Dutch varieties and between themselves in very small degrees of size, form and markings. Careful comparison and tabulations have provided insufficient distinct characters which would warrant separate names, and I refer to them as 'intermediate varieties,' possibly between *C. speciosum* and some southern relation of *C. autumnale*, perhaps *C. Tenorii* or *C. lusitanum*.

They are mentioned here because one or other turns up now and then among stocks exhibited or purchased as *C. autumnale* or *C. speciosum*. They differ from the former by larger size and brighter colouring and from both by the length of the rather narrow segments and a slight trace of tessellation.

The nearest approach to a clue as to origin is provided by the largest one, which was obtained from the late Mrs. Dykes without a name. It is very hard to distinguish it from 'Lilac Wonder,' both fall to the ground on the second day because of their weak and very tall tubes, but the Dykes's plant is rather larger and the flowers are darker, with a pointed apex to the segments which are rounded in 'Lilac Wonder.'

They might be either discarded forms from the seedbeds in which 'Lilac Wonder, and 'Mr. Kerbert' were selected from or perhaps raised by W. R. Dykes from a similar cross, and after his death accidentally mixed and distributed among stocks of *C. speciosum.*

This might account for their appearance at Wisley among purchased stocks. They proved good garden plants and are worth segregating when met with.

XXI

Small-Flowered Species

BY measurement alone it is difficult to draw a good dividing line to separate Colchicums with small flowers from those of medium size. For instance, *C. alpinum* and its closely related species have small flowers, but they stand on tall tubes and obviously resemble and belong to the group including *C. autumnale*, in which some of the species are rather more than medium size. Again the flowers of *CC. troodi* and *Decaisnei* are dwarf, but though the segments are narrow they are so long that they seem related with much larger *CC. lingulatum* and *laetum*.

So for this chapter I will gather together species with flowers smaller and dwarfer than in *CC. alpinum* and *Decaisnei*.

They have characters which distinguish them better than their size of flowers and can be arranged in groups according to the absence or presence of leaves when flowering in autumn, winter or spring.

Those that flower during the darkest days of the year have the smallest flowers and are unsuitable for growing in the open in English gardens, but the vernal species are more robust and in sheltered positions provide a welcome addition to Snowdrops, Eranthis and the early Crocuses. Both groups are worth growing for the alpine house and are of great interest as showing such wonderful adaptations for flowering successfully in sunnier winters of their native eastern and southern homes, by producing a long succession of numerous flowers among protecting leaves close to the ground in bare patches or among short winter herbage.

Except Iris and Narcissus no genus among monocotyledons shows such variation in size of blossoms. Most of these pygmies give out a strong honey-like scent when in sunlight or the warmth of a room.

C. Cupanii of Gussone (1827), often known as *C. Bertolonii* of

Steven (1829), is one of the most widely distributed of these dwarf species which produce leaves and flowers together, being recorded from Greece, Sicily (the type-region), Sardinia, southern France, Tunisia and Algeria. It is accordingly an easy one to collect, but unfortunately does not take happily to cultivation. Those I gathered on Mount Hymettus in Attica, though they flowered for two seasons, failed to become established.

The leaves are narrow, generally two, and appear in autumn with the small rosy-lilac flowers, which have brownish anthers. Its two names commemorate Italian botanists, Francesco Cupani (1657-1710), of Sicily, and Antonio Bertoloni (1775-1869) of Bologna.

The plant figured as "*C. Bertolonii*" in Reichenbach's *Icones Fl. German. 10*, figs. 940-1 (1948), is not this species but *C. hungaricum*:

C. glossophyllum of Heldreich is apparently no more than a variety of *C. Cupanii* with broader and larger leaves, which in some species are as much as an inch broad. It occurs in southern Greece in Messenia and in Attica on Mount Hymettus.

C. pusillum of Sieber is a native of Crete. The plant grown under this name agrees with the description of Halácsy and Stefanoff. It has three narrow leaves and several very small rosy lilac starry flowers. The anthers vary, being yellow in some specimens but nearly black in others. Planted out in a cold frame it has flowered freely over many years from October to December.

C. andrium of Rechinger *fil.* and P. H. Davis is described as a new species in the new Austrian publication *Phyton*, 1, page 221 (1949). Material collected in the Isle of Andros in the Ægean Sea provided the type specimen in the Kew herbarium. It closely resembles *C. pusillum*, differing chiefly in the ciliation of its leaves.

C. peloponnesiacum of Rechinger *fil.* and P. H. Davis, a new species from the Peloponnese, is closely allied to *C. pusillum*. It is described in *Oesterr. Bot. Zeitschrift*, 1948, page 427.

Neither this nor *C. andrium* are as yet in cultivation.

C. hiemale of Freyn is its Cyprian counterpart. I know it only from dried flowering specimens collected in November among

Crocus Veneris and *Ranunculus bullatus*. It has three or four very narrow leaves one-tenth of an inch wide and rosy flowers with segments about three-fifths of an inch long. Thus it may be the smallest of all known Colchicums.

C. creticum of Turrill, described in *Kew Bulletin*, 1939, page 193, was introduced in 1938 by Mr. Peter H. Davis from the Omalo Plain of Crete. It is said to differ from *C. pusillum* in having the membranous tunic not prolonged into a distinct cap above the corm. A specimen kindly sent to me from Kew, in flower but without leaves, in mid-November 1949 seems to differ from *C. pusillum* chiefly in having somewhat larger flowers with dark purplish anthers produced before leaves.

C. Ritchii of R. Brown (*C. aegyptiacum* of Boissier) ranges from Syria and Palestine over Egypt to Tripolitania and has frequently been collected around Alexandria. My attempts to cultivate it have not been successful. Corms received from T. Smith, of Newry, survived for some years in a moraine bed of granite chips, then died out. A later set, collected in Palestine by Mrs. Ruth McConnel in 1943, flowered well the first season, but have since dwindled away. I cannot recommend it for cultivation as the minute nearly white flowers which appear in January are very fugacious. They are interesting, however, on account of the two narrow longitudinal ridges at the base of the perianth segments, which are often entire but occasionally bear one or more small projections described as 'cristate-fimbriate.' Similar outgrowths sometimes occur in *C. Catacuzenium* and are recorded in two Persian species, *C. jesdianum* and *C. palmetorum*. It commemorates Joseph Ritchie (*c.* 1788-1819), a surgeon who collected it near Tripoli. The var. *Guessfeldtianum* of Stefanoff, originally described as a species, *C. Guessfeldtianum*, by Ascherson and Schweinfurth, has downy leaves and comes from Egypt and Sinai.

C. fasciculare of R. Brown was originally described by Linnæus as *Hypoxis fascicularis* from an illustration of a specimen collected near Aleppo. For further details of its history see page 177, under *C. illyricum*. It is a dwarf species with three to seven or more leaves and numerous white or pale rose flowers. Var. *brachyphyllum* of Stefanoff, *C. brachyphyllum* of Boissier, has broader leaves.

*C. Stevenii** of Kunth is figured in the *Botanical Magazine*, t. 8025 (1905) from corms obtained from Georg Egger at Jaffa. The figure portrays what the text rightly describes as a charming plant with comparatively large flowers of better form than is usual among these dwarf species. In 1943 I received a number of corms collected in Palestine by Mrs. McConnel. In some of these corms the foot was about as long as the swollen rounded portion and so much flattened that it suggested the tail of an eel, especially so on account of its waved edge. When they flowered I was disappointed that they had more starry and paler flowers with narrower segments than the plants illustrated. They produced five to twelve narrow leaves. The anthers were yellow. This species proved too delicate for out-door cultivation. It is named after a Finnish botanist, Christian von Steven (1781-1861), director of the Nikita botanic garden in the Crimea, who described *Colchicum speciosum*.

C. Doerfleri of Halácsy is a Macedonian species. It was sent to Wisley by the late Dr. Lemperg, and flowers in February in the alpine house. Through the kindness of Mr. Gould, who sent me a flower and an excellent photograph, I have been able to examine living material.

The flower is very small with narrow, pointed segments, about three-quarters of an inch long above the insertion of the stamens, a bright rosy lilac and of firmer substance than those of *C. pusillum* and other starry-flowered species. In bud it is narrow, tapering to both ends. The stamens are two ranked with versatile anthers, those of the taller stamens dehisced before the others. The anthers are oval in outline, their widest portion about half that of their length. The connective on the upper surface is pale greenish yellow, the flanges are black before dehiscence, the lower surface black all over, the pollen yellow.

The filaments are white coloured olive green at the enlarged base where inserted in the nectarial groove.

It is a two-leaved species, the backs of the leaves pilose with a very fine pubescence and ciliated margins.

The slender outline distinguishes it from *CC. hungaricum*,

* A photograph by Mrs. R. McConnel of wild plants has been published in *Bull. Alpine Garden Soc. 10*, 139 (1942).

N

nivale, libanoticum, and other vernal species which have markedly globular flowers.

C. hungaricum of Janka has been confused with other species under the name *C. montanum.* When I wrote the first edition of this *Handbook* in 1924 the only authoritative botanical survey of the genus Colchicum as a whole was that by John Gilbert Baker in *Journ. Linnean Soc., Bot., 17,* 423-34 (1879). Here and in *Botanical Magazine,* t. 6443 (1879), Baker included under the name *C. montanum* all the spring-flowering Colchicums with dark anthers found 'from Portugal eastward by way of Algeria and Italy to Egypt, Syria, Armenia, Kurdistan and the Caucasus.' Accordingly, when *C. hungaricum* was introduced by the late W. R. Dykes from Croatia, I followed Baker's classification and illustrated it in the first edition of this book as *C. montanum.* In 1925 the late C. C. Lacaita pointed out that Linnæus's *C. montanum* was a mixture of references to *Merendera Bulbocodium* of Spain and *Colchicum alpinum* of the Alps. Loefling's diagnosis quoted by Linnæus refers to the Merendera. The specimen representing *C. montanum* in Linnæus's herbarium has nothing whatever to do with the account printed in his *Species Plantarum,* where its distribution is given as 'Hispania, Helvetia.' A note on the back of the sheet, where data were often recorded in the older herbaria, says 'Habitat in Morea,' which indicates that this specimen came from Greece, not Spain or Switzerland. Lacaita identified it as *C. bulbocodioides* of Bieberstein, not Brotero (i.e. *C. Biebersteinii* of Rouy), but it may be *C. Catacuzenium.* Quite certainly Dykes's Croatian plant is not Linnæus's *C. montanum,* although it received an Award of Merit as such in 1927. Dykes gave it to his friends as his Croatian Colchicum, and for some time it was called *C. montanum* var. *croaticum* or *C. croaticum* in gardens. These garden names were never validly published but appeared in horticultural literature, e.g. *Gardeners' Chronicle* (3), *81,* 120, fig. 62 (1927); *91,* 78, fig. 32 (1932). In 1934 Mr. W. T. Stearn identified it as *C. hungaricum* of Janka and published a full account in the *Journal of the Royal Horticultural Society, 59,* 67-70 (1934). Most of the plants distributed by Dykes had white flowers, but when raised from seed pale lilac forms occur plentifully; all that I have seen have dark purple anthers with orange pollen. It usually has two leaves, less often three, which are short at flowering time but may reach eight inches in length at maturity. Its neat, rather globular flowers are so welcome in January and February that it deserves to be added to every collection of dwarf hardy plants. It grows easily in light soil in a sunny position and may be raised from seed; the seedlings take about three years to reach flowering size. *C. hungaricum*, despite its name, is not widespread in Hungary but occurs there in the south-west comitat, Baranya. It is essentially a northern Balkan species, ranging from Istria, Hungary and Rumania over Croatia and Dalmatia to Hercegovina and Albania.

C. nivale of Stefanoff (*Merendera nivalis* of Stapf) resembles *C. hungaricum* in general appearance, but the bright yellow anthers easily distinguish it. The flowers, as known in cultivation, are always pure white, but pale rose-coloured forms occur in north-western Persia and adjacent Turkish Armenia, where it grows on high mountains and flowers at the melting of the snows. I raised it from seeds collected in Persia by Mr. E. K. Balls.

C. libanoticum of Ehrenberg was collected near snowdrifts on Mount Sannin in the Lebanon range. It is well figured in the *Botanical Magazine*, t. 8015 (1905), which shows both the pale pink and white forms. Boissier described the anthers as yellow (*luteae*) in the type specimens; Stefanoff says they may be yellow or blackish (*luteis vel fuscis*); plants sent to me as this species have the anthers dark purplish before the pollen is discharged. It produces numerous flowers in January and February in the open. They are at first rather dwarf but rise up on the lengthening tubes after a day or so of mild weather and open widely in sunshine; they are then starry and about two inches across.

C. hydrophilum was described by its discoverer Walter Siehe in the *Gardeners' Chronicle*, iii, *29*, 102, fig. 43 (1901). It grows at an altitude of from 3,000 to 6,000 feet in the Taurus Mountains of southern Asia Minor and rejoices in the abundant moisture from the melting snows at its flowering time. This suggested its name, which means 'water-loving.' It is said to differ from *C. libanoticum* in its darker pink and more pointed perianth segments. So far as I can see from plants which I have grown under the name *C. hydrophilum* it is variable in shade of colour and the lighter forms are indistinguishable from the Lebanon plant. Its right to specific rank is questionable. It is figured in the *Botanical Magazine*, t. 8040 (1905).

C. triphyllum of Kunze is a west Mediterranean species. It was first described in 1846 from specimens collected by Willkomm in Spain, but has since been found in Morocco and Algeria. In 1936 Mr. E. K. Balls introduced it into cultivation from Morocco, and his plants received an Award of Merit from the Royal Horticultural Society on February 9th, 1937. Mr. Balls and Dr. Richard Seligman first collected the species on moist turfy slopes, but later found it more robust and in greater quantity higher up on steep hot dry screes at about 10,000 feet. Its distinguishing features are the three leaves (from which it takes its name) and the charming neatness of its globular rosy flowers with rather broad segments, dark bronzy green anthers and bright yellow pollen. It is illustrated in the *Gardeners' Chronicle*, iii, *101*, 255, fig. 102 (1937), and *New Flora and Silva*, *11*, fig. 64, facing page 192 (1939).

C. Catacuzenium comes from Greece. It commemorates a Greek apothecary, Konstantinos J. Katakuzenos, brother-in-law of the botanist Theodor von Heldreich, who collected the type specimens on Mount Parnes, near Athens. It is also recorded from Mounts Parnassus and Chelmos; the illustration in the *Botanical Magazine*, t. 9652 (1943), was drawn from plants collected on these mountains by the Rev. and Mrs. H. P. Thompson. Apparently among the hardiest and prettiest of these winter-flowering species, *C. Catacuzenium* has three glabrous leaves and several rosy flowers with almost black anthers; the segments open out more widely than in *C. triphyllum*. They sometimes bear irregularly developed outgrowths on either side of the segment above the insertion of the stamen similar to those mentioned under *C. Ritchii*.

The following two species, though producing their leaves and flowers together, belong to a different section of the genus from those named above. They have basifixed anthers and unusual flower colouring, the one being yellow, the other white with a distinct pink or violet stripe down each segment.

C. Kesselringii of Regel was named after his son-in-law and partner Jacob Kesselring. It is so distinct a species that, as stated in the *Botanical Magazine*, t. 8055 (1906), 'Regel originally described this plant as generically distinct from Colchicum on the ground that the styles were united. On the receipt of further material Regel found this not to be the case and reduced his genus Synsiphon to Colchicum.' His *Synsiphon crociflorum* of 1879 thus became *Colchicum crociflorum* in 1880, but this name is inadmissible, having been used by Sims in the *Botanical Magazine*, t. 2673 (1826), for what was probably a form of *C. autumnale* collected near Hertford. Stefanoff accordingly renamed Regel's plant *C. Regelii* in 1926; however, Regel himself had described in 1883 a *C. Kesselringii* differing in no essentials from his *C. crociflorum*, and the name *C. Kesselringii* should therefore be adopted for the species. This has evidently a wide range in the mountains of Russian Turkistan, whence it was first introduced into cultivation in 1880 by Albert Regel, son of the botanist Eduard Regel. These corms came from the Alatav Mountains. In 1904 Mr. C. G. van Tubergen, of Haarlem, imported it from the Khokand region. It has, I fear, again disappeared from cultivation. For several seasons the plant throve on a sunny bank of my rock garden, where it always arrested attention, but eventually fell a victim to the depredations of slugs. The flowers appear in January and are slender, with pointed segments, white internally but marked outside with a purple or rosy lilac stripe up the centre of each segment. The anthers are yellow and the styles greenish. The two to seven leaves only just appear above ground at flowering time.

   C. luteum of Baker, figured in the *Botanical Magazine*, t. 6153 (1875), is the only Colchicum known that has yellow flowers. It grows abundantly in parts of Kashmir at 3,000 to 6,000 feet, and also occurs in the mountains of Baluchistan, Afghanistan and Russian Turkistan. Unfortunately it is a very scarce plant in cultivation. It did well in Mrs. Ransome's garden at Ipswich, Suffolk, producing its small but rich yellow flowers in February. Here it suffered the same fate as *C. Kesselringii*, the flowers and young leaves being devoured by slugs as soon as they appeared near the surface.

XXII

Bulbocodium and Merendera

TWO closely related genera have been frequently confused with that of Colchicum, and should be noticed here, though very few of their species are in cultivation.

They differ from Colchicums in that the segments of the flowers are divided right down to the top of the ovary instead of being joined to form a perianth tube. When first the flowers appear above ground they sit so low that the absence of a tube is not noticeable. In their final stage they rise up high enough to split asunder. It can then be clearly seen that the six segments have until then been held together only by the presence of the surrounding soil or the tips of their leaves. On page 13 of my handbook *The Narcissus* I dealt at great length with the history of the ridiculous name Bulbocodium, so I will only repeat some main facts here.

It originated from mistakes of early copyists who joined two words into one in some texts of Theophrastus's *Enquiry into Plants*. It occurs in Book VI, viii, 1, where he mentions *Muscari comosum* among early-flowering plants used for garlands, under the name Bolbos.

He wrote 'τὸ τοῦ βολβοῦ κόδωον' (the head of Bolbos). A copyist rolled the last two words into one as bulbocoduon, which was later latinised as bulbŏcŏdium. This fine-sounding but meaningless name has been widely used ever since, and many false derivations and different meanings have been suggested. There are Greek words of rather similar sound meaning a fleece of wool, a bell or the mouth of a trumpet, and codium was used for a plant like Campanula. Clusius connected bulbocodium with a trumpet daffodil, and Linnæus seems to have been singularly fascinated by the name and attached it irrevocably as a specific for a Narcissus and what he thought to be a Crocus, now *Romulea Bulbocodium*; and as the name of a genus including the plant *B. vernum* as well as a *B. serotinum* which is now Lloydia. Ramond later used it, but invalidly, as a species of Merendera. In no case has it any justifiable meaning in connection with these plants any more than the pious satisfaction and comfort derived by the good old woman from 'that blessed word Mesopotamia.'

Bulbocodium vernum of Linnæus I have collected in flower in June on the slopes between the road and the lake on Mount Cenis.

There is a beautiful figure drawn by Sydenham Edwards in the *Botanical Magazine*, t. 153, also in Redouté's *Liliacées*, vol. IV, 197, we have a very fine one showing the whole plant and also dissection of the flower.

In both of these the artists have drawn the corm from the convex side, making it look as though the flowering shoot sprang from the centre instead of from the base on the flatter side as in a Colchicum.

A transverse section of a corm included in plate 1 of vol. 2 of Retzius's *Observationes Botanicae* clearly shows the position of the main shoot from the same place of attachment as that of the accessory shoot in Edwards's figure.

The block used in the Altera Appendix to Clusius's *Historia* contains two figures named *Colchicum Vernum*, one showing the whole plant in flower, the other with mature leaves and seed pods.

In the former the shoot is shown correctly arising from the base of the old corm, while the second is a very instructive picture of the half-grown new corm alongside the depleted remains of the old.

Parkinson's No. 7 on page 159 of the *Paradisus*, like so many of his figures, is a coarse copy of the good one in *Theatrum Florae*, which is a very fine copy of the flowering plant in Clusius as regards the corm and shoot but not the flowers.

Fig. 1, plate 20, *Autumnus*, of C. de Passe's *Hortus Floridus*, entitled *Colchicum hispan: serotinum* may represent *B. vernum*.

Fig. 1 on plate 27 of Verlot's *Les Plantes Alpines* (1873) is reproduced in Wooster's *Alpine Plants* (1874), vol. 1, plate 35. It shows a very starry form with long pointed segments and paler in colour than the usual form.

Bulbocodium vernum of Linnæus is the only species of this genus in cultivation. It is a common plant in high mountains in central Europe and the Caucasus, flowering soon after the melting of the snow. Its small flowers are much like those of a Colchicum but rather redder in their tone of purple. They appear with the three pointed leaves which at flowering time are shaded with purple.

The base of each segment is furnished with a pair of sharply pointed teeth that point downwards. In the young stage of a flower these interlock and hold the segments so closely together that it appears to possess a tube. In older flowers they no longer function thus and the segments fall asunder in a singularly untidy fashion. Its three styles are welded together into one up to the base of the stigmata.

Bulbocodium vernum has been a favourite plant in English gardens for over three hundred years, but unless specially cared for and frequently replanted in good, well-drained soil does not increase. It is worth growing as it flowers with us about the same time as the Snowdrop.

The genus Merendera differs from the last in having the three styles free to their bases as in Colchicum, and not united as in Bulbocodium, also the greater number of its species flower in autumn.

The generic name Merendera indirectly alludes to this habit.

It was published in 1798 by the French botanist Louis F. E. Ramond, baron de Carbonnière, whose work has priority of publication over that on the Pyrenean flora by Bergeret, who named it Geophila in 1803. Both names were based on the species now called *Merendera montana* (L.) Lange, syn. *Colchicum montanum* L. in part, *Merendera Bulbocodium* Ramond, etc. This is common in mountain pastures in Spain and Portugal and on the French side of the Pyrenees, where Bergeret and Ramond found it. The name Merendera is, however, of Spanish or Portuguese origin, being taken by Ramond from Clusius's Spanish flora *Rariorum aliquot Stirpium per Hispanias observatorum Historia*, 266 (1576), where the common names of the plant, which Clusius named *Colchicum montanum*, are given as 'Merenderas' or 'Quitameriendas.'

The first is derived from the Latin word *merenda** (a midday meal), and the second is still the common Spanish name for this plant. The verb *merendar* in Spanish and Portuguese means to lunch, and has given rise to a number of words connected with food, the feeding of animals and pastures.

So when the autumn rains start the flowering of Merendera, Colchicum and Crocus, the profusion of these lovely flowers warns the shepherds that the time has come to quit the upland pastures, and they call them Quitamerendas.

Ramond used the name Merenderas of Clusius to coin the generic name Merendera. In the Asturias the peasants call it Espanto pastores, the terror of the shepherds.

Merendera montana of Lange (*M. Bulbocodium* of Ramond) is the best-known species and the most frequently met with in gardens.

The corm is small, about a quarter of an inch in diameter, covered with a tough, brown tunic and with a short foot at the base like that of a Colchicum. The flowers appear with the autumn rains at intervals from August to October without leaves. The segments are long and narrow and form a prettily shaped, starry flower, of a very pleasing shade of rosy lilac. A very scarce, but very beautiful, white form has been collected for me in the Asturias Mountains. A form sent to me from Portugal flowers each season early in July and is often the first of all the autumn-flowering bulbous plants to flower, appearing before *Colchicum alpinum* and *Leucoium* (*Acis*) *autumnale*.

The narrow leaves appear in October and remain green, until the capsules rise up in June. It grows and flowers well in beds formed mainly of granite chips in sunny positions in the rock garden, and is a charming plant for such a position.

Redouté's beautiful drawing t. 25, vol. 1 of his *Liliacées*, shows the plant in flower and another with mature leaves and seed capsule in which the old corm, now a shrunken remnant, lies alongside the newly formed one in which the tunic has not yet turned brown.

*It has been suggested that the Latin word *Merenda* is derived from *meridies* (noon) or the verb *merior* (to have a share).

There is a good figure in Verlot's *Plantes Alpines* (1873), fig. 1, plate 29, which is reproduced in Wooster's *Alpine Plants*, plate 16.

M. attica of Spruner is very much like *M. montana*, but is rather larger and brighter in colour and is remarkable for its bluish versatile anthers.

I found it very plentiful close to the edge of the sea by the Bay of Phaleron growing in the sandy ground among *Crocus cancellatus*. There seemed to be a larger and a smaller form, but those I collected did not retain the superior size. It flowers in autumn and was bearing seed pods when I saw it in March 1938.

M. filifolia of Cambessedes grows in the Bouches-du-Rhône, the Balearic Islands and Algeria. It is too small and tender for ordinary English gardens, but a charming pot plant for the alpine house, having such remarkably slender thread-like leaves and pretty pink flowers.

M. trigyna of Stapf also flowers in early spring and has prettier flowers than the last, and when growing happily its rosy flowers are welcome though so small. It has the usual ovoid corm and dark tough tunic of its relations and three narrow leaves appearing with the flowers. The good figure of a mature flower in *Botanical Magazine*, t. 3690 (1838), under the name *M. caucasica* of Bieberstein, shows very clearly the curious auricles or hooks which hold the segments in place while young and the slenderness of the claws where they join the peduncle below the ovary.

This species is commonly known as *M. caucasica*; it has also been called *Bulbocodium trigynum*, *Colchicum trigynum* and *C. caucasicum*.

M. Aitchisonii of J. D. Hooker (*C. robustum* Stefanoff), the subject of t. 6012 in the *Botanical Magazine* (1873), should be called *M. robusta* of Bunge, as he described it in 1847.

It was collected by Dr. Aitchison in the Punjab and sent to Kew, where it flowered in November, but seems to be no longer in cultivation.

The green anthers are very remarkable, and as it represents the farthest eastward range of the genus it would be an interesting plant to grow in a cool house.

M. sobolifera of C. A. Meyer is the same plant as *Bulbocodium hastulatum* of Frivaldsky. It is more curious than beautiful, having minute flowers with narrow, almost threadlike segments, which soon split asunder. It flowers in early spring and is chiefly remarkable for its curious corm formed annually at the end of an underground stolon. It is figured in t. 9576 of the *Botanical Magazine*, vol. 162. The range of this species extends from Bulgaria over Southern Rhodesia and northern Asia Minor to Turkistan and Afghanistan.

XXIII

Notes on the Figures of Colchicum in Parkinson's
Paradisus Terrestris (pp. 153-60; 1629)

PARKINSON has a chapter of five pages and two crude plates devoted to 'the *Colchica* or Medowe Saffrons,' of which he describes nineteen kinds, though it is very doubtful whether he had a first-hand acquaintance with so many. The coarse woodcuts by Switzer are probably all of them copied from other works. The sources of ten (out of fourteen) of these figures are given below:

Page 155

Fig. 1. *Colchicum pannonicum* Parkinson. Source of figure uncertain.

Fig. 2. *Colchicum byzantinum* Parkinson, copied from *Colchicum byzantinum multiflorum* Passe, Hortus Flor. Aut., t. 19 (1614).

Fig. 3. *Colchicum lusitanicum Fritillaricum* Parkinson, copied from *Colchicum neapolitanum* Passe, Hortus Flor. Aut., t. 22.

Fig. 4. *Colchicum neapolitanum Fritillaricum* Parkinson, copied from *Colchicum bysantinum*, Theatrum Florae, t. 41 (1622).

Fig. 5. *Colchicum Fritillaricum Chionse.* Source of figure uncertain.

Fig. 6. *Colchicum hermodactylum* Parkinson, copied from *Colchicum creticum bifolium flores post folia ferens*, Theatrum Florae, t. 41.

Page 159

Fig. 1. *Colchicum montanum hispanicum* Parkinson, copied from *Colchicum montan. hispan.* Clusius, Rar. Pl. Hist. 200 (1601).

Fig. 2. *Colchicum montanum minus versicolore flore* Parkinson, copied from *Colchicum mont. min. versicolore flor.* Clusius, Rar. Pl. Hist., 201.

Fig. 3. *Colchicum versicolor* Parkinson, copied from *Colchicum flore versicolore* Passe, Hortus Flor. Aut., t. 20.

Fig. 4. *Colchicum variegatum alterum* Parkinson. Source of figure uncertain.

Fig. 5. *Colchicum atropurpureum* Parkinson, copied from *Colchicum pannonicum variegatum*, Theatrum Florae, t. 41.

Fig. 6. *Colchicum atropurpureum variegatum*, Parkinson. Source of figure uncertain.

Fig. 7. *Colchicum vernum* Parkinson, copied from *Colchicum montanum vernale flore purpureo*, Theatrum Florae, t. 41 [plus corm from Clusius's Altera Appendix].

Fig. 8. *Colchicum flore pleno* Parkinson, copied from *Colchicum flore multiplici variegatum*, Theatrum Florae, t. 41.

The woodcuts of Clusius's work and the engravings of the *Theatrum Florae* and the *Hortus Floridus* are among the best of their kind. A person acquainted only with the ugly figures in Parkinson's work would never guess that they had degenerated in one stage from such exquisite and accurate originals.

XXIV

Literature on Colchicum

BOTANICAL literature relating to Colchicum is almost as extensive as that on Crocus. The following references will serve as pointers to further sources of information.

1753. LINNÆUS, CARL. *Species Plantarum, 1,* 341-2. Stockholm.

Linnæus was responsible for three Colchicum names, i.e. *C. autumnale* (referring to the common European plant figured in Fuchs, *De Historia Stirpium,* 356: 1542), *C. montanum* (based on a Spanish plant, Clusius's *Colchicum montanum,* now *Merendera montana,* but referring also to the Swiss *C. alpinum*) and *C. variegatum* (the *Colchicum chioense floribus Fritillariae instar tessulatis, foliis undulatis* of Morison, *Hist.,2,* 341, Sect. 4, t. 3, f. 4: 1715).

1807. GAWLER, JOHN BELLENDEN, *afterwards* KER. Colchicum variegatum. *Curtis's Botanical Magazine, 26,* t. 1028.

The plant depicted here appears to be *C. agrippinum* and not the true *C. variegatum* of Linnæus. In the accompanying text Gawler published the name *C. byzantinum,* referring back to the description and figure under the same name in Clusius, *Historia,* 199 (1601).

1850. IRMISCH, THILO. *Zur Morphologie der monokotylischen Knollen- und Zwiebelgewächse.* Berlin.

This elaborate work on the structure and development of bulbs and corms has been described by Agnes Arber as 'the culmination of that exact and fully illustrated morphology, based on naked-eye observations, which flourished up to the middle of the nineteenth century.' Pages 112-20 deal with the corm of Colchicum. An abridged English version was published in *Journal Hort. Soc., London, 8,* 91-124, 207-21 (1853).

1879. BAKER, JOHN GILBERT. A Synopsis of Colchicaceae and the aberrant Tribes of Liliaceae. *Journal Linnean Soc. Bot.*, *17*, 423-57.

This paper contains the first descriptive survey of the genus Colchicum. Here Baker distinguished twenty-nine species. He gave the new name *C. Sibthorpii* to the plant figured in flower, but without leaves, in Sibthorp and Smith's *Flora Graeca*, *4*, t. 350 (1823), as *C. latifolium*, a synonym of *C. byzantinum*. Unfortunately he completely misinterpreted Linnæus's *C. montanum*, under which he grouped a number of species, e.g. *C. Cupanii, C. pusillum, C. Ritchii, C. triphyllum*, now recognised as distinct. Baker described nine species of Merendera.

1882. BOISSIER, EDMOND PIERRE. *Flora Orientalis*, *5*, 155-71. Geneva, etc.

An important account of the species of Colchicum of the Near and Middle East, i.e. those occurring in the territory extending from Greece, Crete and Egypt to India. It describes twenty-nine species of Colchicum, eight of Merendera. Boissier's description of Colchicum as a 'genus quoad specierum distinctionem et determinationem difficillimum et non satis notum' (i.e. a genus of which the species are imperfectly known and most difficult to distinguish and identify) is unhappily as true now as it was then!

1925. LACAITA, CHARLES CARMICHAEL. Colchicum montanum. *Journal Linnean Soc. Bot.*, *47*, 172-4.

This paper calls attention to the misapplication of the Linnæan name *C. montanum* by authors since 1879. Linnæus's references cover both *Merendera montana* (*M. Bulbocodium*) of Spain and *Colchicum alpinum* of the Alps, but the specimen in his herbarium is a Greek species, probably *C. Catacuzenium*, close to *C. Biebersteinii* (*C. bulbocodioides*).

1926 STEFANOFF, BORIS. Monografiya na roda Colchicum. *Sbornik na B'lgarskata Akademiya na Naukitye, Sofiya, 22*, 100 pages. Sofia.

This work is partly in Bulgarian, partly in Latin. The author includes Merendera and Bulbocodium in the genus Colchicum and describes in all sixty-four species. Despite the pains taken by the author in gathering together references and studying herbarium material, it cannot be regarded as a wholly satisfactory work.

1934. STEARN, WILLIAM THOMAS. Colchicum hungaricum Janka. *Journal Royal Hort. Soc.*, *59*, 67-9. Notes on Colchicum. *Journal of Botany*, 72, 341-4.

1951. BURTT, BRIAN LAURENCE. Two new species of Colchicum. *Kew Bulletin*, 1950, 431-4.

A GLOSSARY OF THE BOTANICAL TERMS
USED FOR CROCUS AND COLCHICUM

Annuli	Rings of membrane forming the lower portion of the corm tunic in certain species.
Anther	The upper portion of a stamen which contains the pollen.
Basal spathe	A tubular membrane springing from the summit of the corm and wrapping the flower stalk and ovary in certain species.
Basal tunic	A separate small portion of tunic at the base of a corm.
Blade	The outer and thinner edges of a leaf, rolled back when young, expanded at maturity.
Cap	An upward prolongation of the fibres or membrane of a corm tunic.
Capsule	The seed vessel.
Caruncle	A fleshy protuberance on the seed.
Channel	A longitudinal groove in the leaf.
Ciliated	Fringed with fine hairs.
Claw	The narrowed lower portion of the tepals in Bulbocodium and Merendera.
Corm	A solid bulb-like underground stem.
Corm tunic	The fibrous or membranous wrapping of the corm, renewed annually.
Diphyllous	Two-leaved, used of the *proper spathes, see* under Spathe.
Extrorse	Anthers opening on the outer side.
Filament	The stalk of an anther.
Glabrous	Smooth, without hairs.
Introrse	Anthers opening on the inner side.
Keel	A thickened central ridge on the under side of the leaf.

Membranous	A skin of homogeneous tissue forming the tunic of some species.
Monophyllous	One-leaved, used of the *proper spathe, see* under Spathe.
Ovary	The immature seed vessel.
Perianth	The coloured floral envelopes, representing the sepals and petals.
Perianth tube	The slender tubular portion of the flower between the ovary and the segments, serving instead of a stalk.
Pistil	The female organ consisting of ovary, style, and stigma.
Proper spathe	*See* under Spathe.
Protogynous	When the stigmata are receptive before the anthers have ripe pollen.
Reticulate	With netted fibres. Used of the corm tunic.
Scape	The flower stalk below the ovary.
Segments	The divisions of the perianth, six in number, arranged in an outer and inner series.
Sheathing leaves „ *scales*	A strong wrapping of three to five tough and fleshy tubular leaves arising from the inner wrapping of the corm, and enclosing the leaves and flowers until they reach the ground level.
Spathe	Thin semi-transparent bracts that enclose the flower when young.
„ , *basal*	A spathe springing from the summit of the corm.
„ , *proper*	One or two spathes springing from just below the ovary. When one only is present it is termed monophyllous, and if there are two the plant is said to be diphyllous.
Stamen	The male organ consisting of anther and filament.
Stigma	The upper part of the pistil which receives the pollen.

Stigmata	⎫ The three divisions into which the upper part
Stigmatic branches	⎭ of the pistil of a Crocus is divided.
Tepal	A term now used for a perianth segment.
Throat	The funnel-shaped orifice of the flower where the perianth tube and perianth segments join.
Tube	*See* Perianth tube.
Tunic	*See* Corm tunic.

Index

This index compiled by W. T. Stearn supplements the text by giving concise references to the books and periodicals where the specific names of Colchicum and Crocus were first published. B.M.=Curtis's Botanical Magazine; *Bull.*=Bulletin; *G.C.*= The Gardeners' Chronicle; *J.*=Journal.

Agrotis segetum (Turnip Moth), 16, 71
Aitchison, J. E. T., 202
Anemone blanda, 100
Angleshade Moth (*Phlogophora meticulosa*), 16
Ankara Crocus, 95
Anthers of Colchicum, 153; of Crocus, 25
Ants and seed dispersal, 27, 158
Arber, A., quoted, 206
Arnott, S., quoted, 175
Atchley, S. C., 100
Autran, E. J. B., 45
Autumn Crocus, 154; of Halifax, 33
Autumnal Crocuses, 30, 37, 52
Azalea mollis, 15

Backhouse, R. O., 173
Baker, J. G., 25, 139, 207; quoted 109, 194
Balansa, B., 106
Balls, E. K., 127, 133, 196; quoted, 38
Barr, P. R., 4, 43, 46
Bees, 26
Bertoloni, A., 191
Bibliography of Colchicum, 206-208; of Crocus, 135-140
Birds as enemies of Crocus, 16
Boissier, E. P., quoted, 207
Bornmüller, J. F. N., 173
Bulbocodium Linnæus, Sp. Pl., 294 (1753), Gen. Pl. 5th ed., 142 (1754); 198
B. hastulatum Frivaldsky in Flora (Regensburg) 19: 434 (1836), a synonym of *Merendera sobolifera*; 203
B. serotinum Linnæus, Sp. Pl. 294 (1753), a synonym of *Lloydia serotina*; 198
B. vernum Linnæus, Sp. Pl. 294 (1753); 198, 199, **200**
Burtt, B. L., 89, 90, 180, 208

Cakes, Saffron, 63
Cambessedes, J., 85
Carthamus tinctorius, 63
Catocala nupta (Red Underwing Moth), 24.
Celandine Crocus, 104
Chittenden, F. J., 186
Cloth of Gold Crocus, 94
Cloth of Silver Crocus, 87
Clusius, C. (L'Ecluse, C. de), 94, 98, 135, 136, 168, 170, 179, 200
Colchicine, 158, 159
Colchicum Linnæus, Sp. Pl. 341 (1753), Gen. Pl. 5th ed. 159 (1754); 153 *et seq.*
  anther colour, 153
  bibliography, 206-208
  botanical characters, 27, 154
  classification difficulties, 154, 207
  corm development, 155
  cultivation, 153, 160
  dormant period, 155
  garden value, 153
  hybrids, 185
  leaves, 153, 158
  literature, 206-208
  medicinal value, 159
  name, 159
  perianth, 153, 154
  poisonous properties, 158-60
  remedy for gout, 159
  seeds, 158
  stamens, 154
  styles and stigmata, 154, 161
  tessellation of, 154, 179
Colchicum aegyptiacum Boissier, Diagn. i. 5: 66 (1844), a synonym of *C. Ritchii*; 192
C. agrippinum Baker in J. Linn. Soc. Bot. 17: 425 (1879); 158, 160, **182**, 183, 184, 185, 206
C. algeriense Battandier & Trabut, Fl. Alg. Monocot. 76 (1895); 164